The late Kit Pedler was a docto scientist of great distinction. T research papers on the eye and v of short stories and science fic environmental affairs on both ra very well known as a teacher of environmental science.

Together with Gerry David, Kit Pedler created and wrote the enormously successful television series 'Doomwatch'.

KIT PEDLER

The Quest for Gaia

A Book of Changes

Paladin

An Imprint of Grafton Books
A Division of HarperCollinsPublishers

Paladin
An Imprint of GraftonBooks
A Division of HarperCollins*Publishers*
77–85 Fulham Palace Road,
Hammersmith, London W6 8JB

Published in Paladin Books 1991
9 8 7 6 5 4 3 2 1

Previously published by Granada Publishing 1981

First published in Great Britain by
Souvenir Press Ltd 1979

A CIP catalogue record for this book
is available from the British Library

ISBN 0-586-08365-0

Printed and bound in Great Britain by
Collins, Glasgow

Set in Baskerville

The quotation on p. 65 comes from *Poems 1913–1956* by
Bertolt Brecht, edited by John Willett and Ralf Manheim.
Copyright Eyre/Methuen 1976.

To Gaians the world over

Contents

Foreword

This book is about personal changes which could evolve from a rejection of the industrial society. It is not about doom or catastrophe, but suggests an optimistic expansion of human consciousness which could develop from life in a post-industrial age.

It is also about a goddess.

I have assumed, right from the beginning, that everyone knows all about environmental pollution and that everyone is fully aware that our present activities are not only destroying the life process of our planet, but also using up its resources in a way which makes our future wholly unsustainable.

I have also assumed that no aspect of this rapidly darkening situation will improve without radical alterations to the way we live, and that the changes necessary will amount to an almost complete rejection of the values and artefacts of the industrial society.

But there is no point in proposing changes unless they lead to an improvement in human creativity and happiness; and it is my strong belief that if we can relearn a way of life which is, as far as possible, removed from the industrial process, then we can not only live within the limits set by the earth, but also reawaken an expanded sense of vision and consciousness which our ancestors once had as a natural birthright. A vision which I have almost entirely suppressed by accepting the glittering products of industrialism.

Before I began to write, I was seized with an unbearable frustration and anger about the destructive effect we are having on the planet. And then I realized the very obvious truth that the anger and frustration were both directed against myself, since I was fully parasitic upon the industrial society which I hold to be the main villain of the piece. And so the book is about changes which are practicable on an individual level and changes which I am in the process of carrying out for myself.

I now intend to live in a way that has as little to do with the industrial society as possible. For I believe that when historians of the future assess its overall effect on people, they will decide that this society was not only dehumanizing and despoliating, but above all, overwhelmingly ugly.

Nothing is perfect and I am finding it difficult to abandon the ordinary pursuits of a relatively affluent middle-class hedonist. So the book is partly a way of making a personal and public declaration which will keep me to a continued course of action and so reduce my personal level of hypocrisy.

The most serious error of exploitative technologists has been to assume that nature is neutral, unthinking and passive: merely a complex process to be dominated and manipulated. I hold that the reverse is true and that the life process around us is driven by an intelligence which is fully capable of recognizing and repairing damage done to itself.

And so this book is also about a revolution and a revolutionary, but it is not about ideologies of the left or the right and not about human-centred ideas of justice and equality. No economic analyses and no classifications of relative human merit are offered, but ideas about survival are.

It is my main thesis that a new revolutionary has awakened, beside whom human pretenders to the role are as children.

This entity is the most determined and dangerous opponent ever to face us and needs no party, arms or supporters. It functions adequately by itself.

It is neither kind nor cruel, moral nor immoral.

It cares nothing for the continuance of the human race and can design the death of man, woman or child as and when appropriate.

It possesses ancient wisdom, is wholly integrated in its purpose and cannot be defeated, but only joined.

It is ageless and non-ageing and has one purpose and one purpose only.

And so I have posed the problems of survival against the

inhuman wrath of this entity and given an account of the changes demanded by our final and most determined opponent.

I do not intend what follows to be a moral statement, but an account first of a route to survival and then of a means of re-establishing a lost sense of vision, which was once as natural to us as the ability to see with our eyes.

The name of the revolutionary is Gaia.

Introduction

Gaia is one of the names given to the goddess of the earth, and it was once believed that she was the creator of Gods, the earth-mother and bestower of all abundance. She was also called Ge or Gaea by other cultures and was prayed to as Dano, Nammu or Coatlicul.

Myths of the earth goddess differ in detail, but all have the common idea that the earth is not a dead body but is inhabited by a spirit which is its life and soul. All agree that the earth spirit is female and will give nourishment to those who shelter in her womb.

I use the name Gaia not to propose a human feminine goddess, but to encompass the idea that the entire living pelt of our planet, its thin green rind of life, is actually one single life-form with senses, intelligence and the power to act.

Stretching from man to the worm, from the fishes of the abyss to the yoghurt bacterium, and from the moulds of decay to the birds riding the sky, I hold that there is but one single interwoven web of life and that our own kind was, until recently, an integral part of this single magnificent entity.

I have chosen 'Gaia' rather than the other names because I think it is a beautiful name and extends naturally into the idea of Gaian living or 'Gaianism'.

We live in a society based upon science and technology and so it is here that we must look for the roots of error and of change. But first I want to make a clear distinction between different breeds of scientists and technologists.

During my career as a research scientist I met and was happily influenced by men and women whose main purpose in life was to understand the beauties of the natural world in their own terms of respectful reason: people who fell in love with an aspect of nature and who sought to understand it a little better.

To these imaginative people I would reapply the old name, 'natural philosophers', as my own act of respect; but they are as different as it is possible to be from those I shall call the 'technologist-toymakers'.

The word technologist is usually defined to mean a 'practitioner of the industrial arts', but here I use the term to describe a variant of the toolmaker scientist; the person who sees the process of reason as a means only to the end of a new structure or tool; a person without values, respect or love; a person who creates a system or a tool just because it is possible. This is the 'technologist-toymaker', whose prime ethos of exploitation is completely opposed to the loving and respectful credo of the natural philosopher.

The technologist-toymaker is the designer of the electric toothbrush and the anti-personnel shrapnel grenade: toys for tearing the gums or the bodies of people.

This compulsive and often exultant toolmaking has led to the celebration of *reductionism*, which is a method of thinking based on the idea that the whole can be fully understood by analysing its parts.

Reductionism is opposed to *holism*, which is based on the concept that the whole is more than the sum of the parts, and that true understanding can emerge only by making this assumption.

Reductionists also offer the fiction that life began only as a development of chemical interactions; that the first cells emerged by accident in a warm primeval soup, and that no other factors need to be considered.

The toymaker reductionist further holds that the earth and the universe is a neutral, insensate aggregation of energy and matter that has no connection with or interest in the affairs of men. Reductionists thus assert that there are no values in the universe; no beauty, no rhythm and no regard, care or love, just systems for analysis and exploitation.

This tragic and limited view of nature has directly generated the basic tenet of the industrial society: that it is perfectly in order to develop more powerful ways to manipulate nature with no other consideration in mind.

As a consequence, the control of 'high technology' over nature appears complete. It is simply a matter, say the technocrats, of designing new processes to create any artefact either for increased control or for rectification of an error. No consideration is given to the possibility that nature, the earth organism, Gaia, may not be neutral nor indeed be merely a sum of its parts. Such an idea threatens the intellectual power structure of the technocrats and is dismissed as emotional or irrational argument.

The reductionist illusion of power and control is mistaken because it takes no account of this possibility: that ever since our toolmaking capabilities developed to a point where we were capable of producing changes on a planetary scale, our activities have been observed and counter-action begun. This is my first point. The observer is not a decent, right-thinking and humane human being, full of liberal virtues or a sense of what is fair and just. And counter-action is not to be understood in terms of human conflict. What is at stake is the earth organism's primary search for stability.

The 'Gaia hypothesis'[1] suggests that the earth and its atmosphere can best be looked at not as a lifeless physico-chemical construct, but as a living entity with the equivalent of senses, intelligence, memory and the capacity to act. I shall extend this idea.

Gaia is non-human. She is the earth spirit, she is life, the ground, the air, the water and the interaction between all their inhabitants. Within the fabric of Gaia, the earth organism or the earth spirit, whichever term you prefer, there is an interwoven and intelligently driven web which searches for balance, continuance and stability.

About twelve thousand years ago, man discovered how to grow food in one place. Before that, he was nomadic and forced to move from one exhausted hunting site to another to find new food. During his last nomadic phase, he had already been gathering wild grasses to eat. Then he planted the seeds and

---

[1] The scientific basis of the 'Gaia hypothesis' is entirely due to James Lovelock, FRS, and his various collaborators who have published a number of works describing and developing the idea. I believe it to be the most important single scientific work of recent time. I am delighted here to pay tribute to their originality and courage.

produced the first grain crop. These men, the first farmers, were forced by circumstances to live alongside the stream of Gaia. They did not farm intensively, they did not produce significant pollution from their fires and sewage and they scarcely used the minerals of the earth. They had no written language and only the most basic toolmaking capability. They lived in this way by necessity rather than choice and worshipped gods of grain, fertility and love. They did not worship their own abilities. Despoliation of the earth would have been anathema to them, because it would have reduced their food supply.

There was no particular time or place on the earth where this tenable relationship broke down. The industrial revolution is often singled out as the main point of change, and in some ways this appears to be true since the development of engines and large-scale machinery led to a sudden and massive exploitation of the environment. But there has always been an evolutionary pressure behind the development of knowledge which made the industrial revolution inevitable. The geometry of Euclid was the direct precursor of the Apollo rocket.

The 'population explosion' has also been singled out as the prime cause for our present situation, and frightening accounts of decreased doubling times and incipient famine have appeared. There is obviously a real population problem, just as there is a parallel food supply problem. But to say that either is a principal cause is to avoid what I believe to be the central issue. Moreover, population increases are beginning to show unpredicted changes in direction. Urban population figures are beginning to fall and the *technogenic diseases*, the diseases traceable to high technology, are exacting an increasing toll. Both these factors are, I hold, part of the stabilizing process of Gaia. This process I shall develop in later sections.

We have misunderstood the problem completely. There is no value in blaming the industrial revolution, the population explosion or some other physical activity of man. It has been our most consistent conceit that our activities must always be primary rather than incidental or secondary.

There is no way in which contemporary industrial practices are compatible with the changes and restraints demanded by Gaia. No amount of pollution or heat loss reduction in an industrial plant could ever justify its continued existence, if it makes throw-away plastic cups – even when the bankrupt mythologies of 'growth', 'market' and 'profit' seem to justify making throw-away cups as a highly profitable enterprise.

There is no point in counting money if you live on a charred cinder.

Anthropocentric explanations avoid the main issue. They are important metaphors, but offer no glimpse of the heart of the matter. They are relatively guilt-free models which suggest modifications and 'technical fixes' as means of improvement rather than radical change.

Survival in the future will depend entirely on whether or not we can find a way back to a non-exploiting relationship with Gaia.

The problem is *not* merely that we have plundered the earth's resources and polluted our surroundings. This is obvious and true, but the harsh point is that we shall *never* stop doing so until we have restructured our lifestyle to a point where it *is* compatible with the real nature of the life process of which we were once a part. There is, for example, no real advance in living in a commune if, at the first sign of illness, the communards start taking antibiotics made by the large-scale oil-based pharmaceutical industry outside the boundary of the commune. Communards are nearly all to some degree parasitic on the very society they hold to be so objectionable – as indeed I found myself to be before embarking on the project to change my own lifestyle on which this book is based.

The blueprint for a sustainable future can only appear if we look outside our own lives to Gaia, and to make that relationship the *primary*, and not the secondary, centre of our attention. Everything we do must now relate outwards to this goal and not inwards to our own needs defined in our own terms. This we must do not for moral reasons, but, like the first farmers, so that we can continue to live on the earth, and so that our children do not become victims of the cruel hoax of being encouraged to plan for a non-existent future.

We have to develop a way of life in which we come second and base our living on an *extra-human ethic*.

This demands a radical change of direction and habit. Every

aspect of our day-to-day life will have to be analysed and altered until it accords with the natural currents and stabilizing systems of Gaia. Only then can we hope to continue our existence on this very small planet.

We must therefore develop an entirely new body of knowledge: *Gaianism* perhaps.

At least two other problems have to be faced before any real dis-assembly of our present way of life can begin. The first is that our minds are becoming ruthlessly decerebrated. We are being progressively stripped of skills by the seductions of the media and the commercial world. And many of us are made to work ever harder at dehumanizing tasks to earn money to pay artificially inflated prices to acquire glittering artefacts. They have no other function than that of paying respect to a machine society which actually decreases the quality of life and suppresses the creative impulse.

The second problem is political. There is an accelerating race between the gentle freedoms of the individual and the increasingly efficient control processes of ruthlessly organized national bureaucracies. Any semblance of democracy is being ground out of existence by the *dictatorship of the technocrat*, and an unholy bargain has been struck between those who govern and those who profit by the high technological process. This sinister development is equally a product of communist and capitalist societies: it has come about only six years before 1984.

I believe in the creative human spirit and its capacity for change. I believe that the changes I shall propose could begin to return to a tired and sickened people that self-regard which is being crushed out of them, by the criminal activities of the commercial–government axis and the bullying of the bureaucrat. I also believe that the adoption of the changes can lead to a real and expanded sense of vision.

This book then is not written for the ideologists of the left or right, for they are already immersed in the self-destructive task of following their own critical path towards maximum power. They are locked in a shell which produces only cynicism, corruption and illness. The necessary changes which are now so clearly demanded from us will spring only from individuals who are properly informed and willing to change radically. Capitalism in this respect is as antique an ideology as communism. But I shall suggest that *Gaianism* is an entirely logical basis for equality among people.

There is no doubt that the revolution – what I shall call the last revolution – will occur, and that the revolutionary will offer no compromise. Our technologies are grossly overshot and unstable and will hurtle through greater and greater amplitudes of instability before they collapse. So we have to bring about radical changes in the way we live, like it or not.

Although we have no choice, this is not a cause for pessimism. We will certainly have to dis-assemble and repudiate much of our present way of life in the developed countries; but although this sounds as if I am suggesting some reactionary and joyless return to the rigours of the Middle Ages, this is not the case. I am not suggesting either that we should suddenly throw away half our knowledge. It is after all only a small step from censorship to another 'burning of the books'. All we have to do with knowledge is to reapply it to new imperatives. There is no such thing as alternative technology, only appropriate technology for a Gaian future: Gaian technology.

What I do suggest is that much of the present body of scientific and technical knowledge has been used by the toymakers to threaten our future. It is up to us to reassemble a more rewarding and happy life based upon a detailed co-existence with Gaia.

I am not suggesting either that we shall be forced to live a grey existence dressed in rags and tip-toeing about to avoid breaking a blade of grass. Gaianism will allow us to use the riches of our planet in a way which can generate a much deeper and lasting sense of happiness, and above all a fresh sense of vision and enrichment of the human condition.

In much the same way as the malignant cells of cancer invade and destroy the normal tissue of the body, so do the affairs and processes of the toymaker technocrats invade and destroy the balanced and stable earth organism. A cancer could be prevented if it were possible to restore the anarchic and predatory behaviour of its cells to a controlled relationship with the cells of the body.

Malignant cells have no senses, language or response variation, whereas man has senses, intelligence, language and tool-making ability, and is consciously able to change his responses to outside variation. Above all, we have freedom of choice and therefore responsibility.

We have all the necessary information and skill to alter our way of living so that it falls within the limits of stability set by Gaia. We have choice and a mind; the cancer cell does not.

Most of our cultural patterns assume that there will be a natural continuance of man; that come pestilence, war or famine, a few people will always survive to evolve and continue.

I now disbelieve this myth entirely. For the first time in our history, we are facing the likelihood that in our present state we are seeing the last generations of dominance of our species.

It is as if we have lived through the whole of our history shutting out one half of knowledge. Through the centuries we have groped our way towards ideals of 'human progress' and 'human growth' with nothing outside ourselves in mind, and now the trap built by all those predatory ages is beginning to spring.

Our magnificent success as toymakers has given us the misleading belief that our understanding of nature has also been successful. But the reverse is the case. Because we have developed sciences and technologies which are entirely self-centred, we have failed to consider the extra-human situation developing alongside this indulgence.

The term *symbiosis* describes two organisms which live in active balance by exchange one with the other. By analogy, our future on this planet depends on redeveloping a lifestyle which is equally symbiotic with Gaia. I say redeveloping, because the knowledge necessary to do this is only something we have forgotten, not something we need to acquire. We already have enough ideas for the millennium.

We can no longer get by with general and paternalistic notions about 'living in balance with nature'. We have to analyse each and every aspect of our lives to see how they can all be altered in detail, if we are to achieve active symbiosis with the earth organism.

* * *

This book is in three parts. The first sets out the basic driving forces of the earth organism, and the manner of the coming revolution.

The second is a blueprint for refutation of the industrial society.

The third is a description of how the changes which follow this refutation can enable us to resume a way of life by which we can not only achieve a sustainable future in practical terms, but also attain an expanded consciousness of the life-form which surrounds us and a deeper and richer view of our relationship with that life-form.

PART ONE

The Anatomy of an Angry Goddess

1

Sun is Life

To find out how the human body works, we study its anatomy and physiology. To understand Gaia we can do the same.

Humans need food as an external source of energy. So does Gaia; her food is the radiation of the sun.

The earth organism is protoplasm, chlorophyl, the earth, sky, bacteria, viruses and people. They all consume energy.

The sun supplies most of the incoming energy of the planet. Without it there would be no life and the earth would be permanently frozen and silent. There would be no springs or summers and no green leaves or children.

One surprising discovery about energy is that it cannot be defined. Everyone knows that there *is* energy in heat, light, electricity, fossil fuels and the atom, and that there is potential energy in a raised weight at the end of a rope looped over a pulley. But it is impossible to isolate a pure 'essence of energy' and cork it up in a bottle.

Energy is an idea of a something which can only be *converted* or transformed. The energy in coal can be converted into steam which drives a turbine, the energy in sugar can be converted into the movements of a muscle, and energy from the sun can be converted into all the processes of life. Figure 1 is a simplified layout of the energy conversion and transformation which goes on inside Gaia. Scientists call it the planetary energy flow. I call it the flow of life in the earth organism. The circulation in the body of a Goddess.

Radiation energy from the sun pours in from space. Thirty per cent is immediately lost again to space by reflection and dispersion in the atmosphere, and another 47 per cent is absorbed and reflected from the land, the oceans and the green leaves of plants and trees. Twenty-three per cent is converted in the weather and

Energy & The Flow of Life

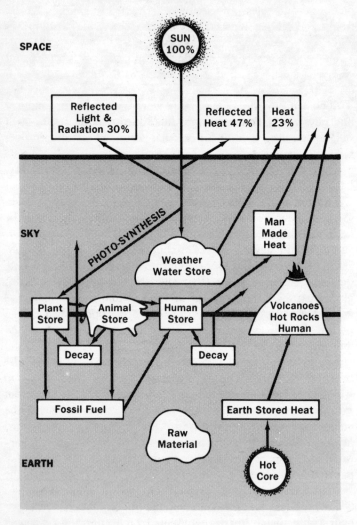

Figure 1

water cycles of the planet and a tiny amount is transformed into wind and waves. An even smaller part comes into the biosphere in the form of tidal energy driven by the gravities of the earth, moon, sun complex, and there is a small contribution of heat from the earth's stored heat coming from volcanoes, hot springs and rock conduction.

The whole is a seething, flowing mass of movements and change. Like the human body, nothing is ever still in the earth organism.

Not all the energy of the biosphere is in this boiling state of flux however; a little is stored. Plants store it in the form of sugar. Animals store it in their flesh. Humans store it in man-made structures as well as in their flesh. Plants and animals decay and slowly turn into fossil fuels like oil and coal. One day, far in the future, all the bodies of all the men and women and creatures who have ever lived may be fossil fuel again. A cycle will be complete and some visitors from space may use us to light their lamps.

Finally, the process upon which the whole of the life of Gaia and ourselves depends uses up less than 1 per cent of the whole incoming energy from the sun. This magical sequence is called 'photosynthesis' and our survival is entirely dependent on it.

It is a sensitive and beautiful network of events which drives the life process of the earth organism. It drives plants which then grow, reproduce and decay back into the earth. Once plants grow, the entire process of life can proceed in an interlocked chain of events which I have called the *solar drive chain*.

Photosynthesis is the process whereby plants convert the abundance of the sun into life (Fig. 2). Human beings make metal solar panels to absorb and store the energy of the sun, plants grow solar panels called leaves. A leaf is a small master-work of design, a beautiful and microscopically elegant solar panel. The details of the photosynthesis which goes on inside it are still incompletely understood, but the principle is simple. Carbon dioxide and sunlight are taken in by the plant. Carbo-hydrates are made and stored in the plant and oxygen is released back to the atmosphere. Then the energy in the stored carbo-hydrate is reconverted to make the parts of the plant by a second great process called respiration.

Cycles of Life

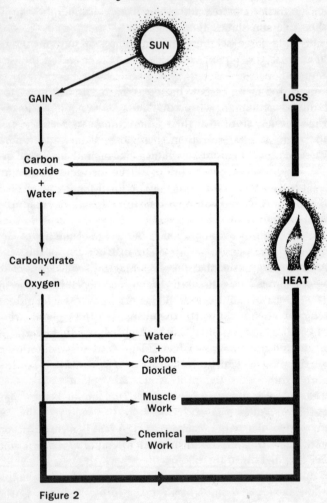

Figure 2

Respiration is the combination of carbohydrates with oxygen to release the energy stored in the carbohydrate. This again releases carbon dioxide and water for use in photosynthesis: a harmonious and elegantly simple cycle of events in which solar energy is trapped, stored and released on a continuous basis. As long as the sun shines there is perpetual motion in the earth organism; as long as its lovely light fills the sky, life continues easily, quietly and in perfect balance.

Respiration happens either in the plant, or later, when the energy stored in its carbohydrates is released: in the bodies of the animals or humans who eat it.

But one event of overriding importance happens during photosynthesis and respiration. Heat is released.

The amount of energy lost in this heat is very, very small, but it is of central importance. The increase in surface warmth of the human body after a meal is one indication of how little the heat loss really is. But the reason why this tiny loss is so vital is that the energy in that heat is dispersed and gone for ever. It soaks into a planet-wide heat sink. And this means that the process whereby we live is not a perfect cycle; it leaks.

All the time that sunlight is streaming into the fabric of the life-form some of it is dissipating irrecoverably. Heat is flowing out of a myriad points on the planet. Again this does not seem to be very important, since the sun shows every evidence of being stable, apart from a few annual wobbles in output. So, why is this tiny amount of lost energy so important to an understanding of Gaia, and what has it to do with the solar drive chain?

The answer is unexpected.

Heat is the ultimate pollutant.

To justify this strange claim, I want to look at just one scientific law which has withstood all attempts to refute it since it was first developed.

2

Disorder is Death

Scientific 'laws' do not depict cosmic truths, they are only celebrations of temporary consistencies: fairly reliable general statements about particular events. It is a scientific 'law' that light travels in straight lines, but sometimes it goes round corners, so the law is not true but only gives a fair approximation. A good scientist with a degree of cheek, presented with a law as truth, automatically attempts to refute it.

The second law of thermodynamics is probably the most inviolate 'law' in the whole of science. Thermodynamics deals with the flow of heat and almost as many word forms of the second law exist as there are thermodynamicists, so I have written it in a form that suits the main concept of this book.

All energy used by living and non-living processes eventually degrades to irrecoverable waste heat.

First, let me explain the use of the word 'degrade'. When the engine of a car burns fuel to turn the wheels, the high temperature of the burning fuel is called high grade energy, since it can produce work to turn the wheels. The diffuse low temperature of the heat leaking away from the radiator, the exhaust and the body of the engine is called low grade since it cannot do further work. *High grade*, then, means localized, high temperature and work-producing, and *low grade* means diffuse, low temperature and useless for work. There is absolutely no practical way of getting back *all* the low grade energy from the engine to make it do further work, so it too is lost to the planetary heat sink. High grade energy then inevitably degrades to low grade energy.

This leads to the second fundamental idea about the way nature works, and this has been given a special name by thermodynamicists. It is basic to my general theme and it is called *Entropy* (illustrated in Fig. 3, page 32).

Again there are many different word descriptions of this odd concept, and I have chosen one which fits the need to understand Gaia:

All processes tend to disorder.

Put sticks and paper together and light a bonfire. The orderly pile disorders into a mass of flame, heat, smoke and ash which can *never* be reassembled again into an orderly pile. If a gun is fired there is no process whereby the noise, flame, heat and speeding bullet can spontaneously or otherwise be forced up the barrel again to re-form the cool loaded cartridge. Both are one-way events.

Every time we walk a pace forward, respiratory processes in the body burn a little *ordered* carbohydrate to power the muscles of our legs, and some *disordered* waste heat has been lost without recall from the surface of the body.

Each and every time a single bacterium moves forward a millionth of an inch it releases a few micro-calories of waste disordered heat, and every time a jet plane cuts its way through the air it leaves behind a massive swathe of irrecoverable heat which disperses into the planetary heat sink in total disorder.

An increase in disorder, then, is an increase in entropy and a decrease in disorder is a decrease in entropy.

But can it be generally true that all processes tend to disorder? If a plant gathers disordered and dispersed sunlight and dis-ordered and dispersed carbon dioxide and blends them with water by photosynthesis; if it then makes and stores ordered energy as carbohydrates, it has apparently decreased disorder and thus entropy. Is it not also true then, that if a power station burns fuel to make steam to drive generators to make ordered electricity, it too has increased order and decreased entropy?

There is one fundamental difference between living systems and the activities of technical man. A living plant does indeed reduce entropy; but when it comes to the end of its natural life, in its normal state it decays back into the earth and is partly recycled as nutrients for new plant growth. The total amount of disorder it produced during its lifetime was the very small amount of waste heat it released to the air from its internal

Entropy & Life

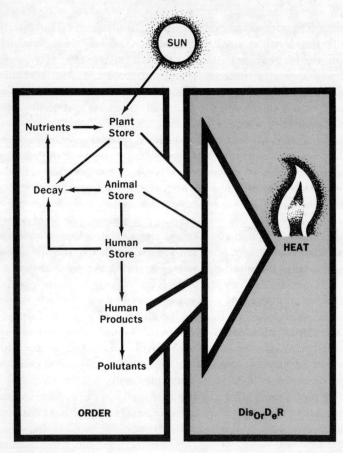

Figure 3

processes and this is easily paid back by decay and recycling. An animal also consumes, respires, releases waste heat, dies and decays back into the earth. But technical man is completely different from all other life-forms.

Technical man can indeed produce very large reductions in disorder in one place, but in so doing he creates a very much larger disorder elsewhere.

If the electricity company running the power station generates and delivers electricity into a national grid system, only 28 per cent of the energy in the fuel turns into electricity. The remaining 72 per cent is released as waste heat, entropy or disorder. The process has therefore contributed massively to the net disorder of the planet, and the electricity generating company should more properly be *a waste heat generating company*, since its prime product is entropy not electricity.

Technical man produces a massive increase in entropy and is therefore incompatible with the low entropy systems of Gaia.

This statement is really at the heart of the matter, and is the basis of the changes we have to make to avoid the stabilizing responses of the earth organism.

It follows that: *The only way to achieve a sustainable future for our species is to develop a way of life which contributes no net entropy increase to the planet.*

In a functional high technology society, there is no conceivable way in which this ideal can be achieved. But it is the main principle on which this book is based, not because it is moral or good, but because it is a question of survival.

Without man, all the biological systems of the earth organism are more or less in entropic balance, so long as the sun continues to give out its abundance. Somewhere, in the millennia to come, the sun itself will grow cold and then all the processes driven by it will slow down and stop. There may be a time – observed by no human – when nothing at all ever happens on the planet. In a perpetual silence there would be no winds, no currents or waves, no temperature or pressure differences and no flow of energy. This is sometimes called the *universal heat death*, when there would be only matter and no energy. There would be no celebrations of technical success in that Valhalla; our remains would long since have crumbled into a tomb of absolute silence and inaction. Nothing would ever happen again.

If the second law of thermodynamics and the concept of entropy are inviolate, another statement follows which is central to the development of a sustainable future.

We are the only species ever to have removed dependence on the solar drive chain.

Without sun, there is no animal or plant life, except for a very few specialized organisms living in caves and other dark places. We are entirely different, we use the fossil fuels coal and oil. So it is true to say that our present high technology is based not on solar energy but on stored solar energy. Both the oil and coal stored in the ground were once a living part of the earth organism and were created by the sun. It is not only a problem that these resources are finite – this is perfectly obvious – but that by using them we have created a massive quantity of entropic disorder.

This entropy appears in the form of waste heat and pollutants, which degrade biologically balanced systems and destroy the balanced systems of the air, ground and water.

There is no such thing as an energy crisis, there is enough coal in the ground for hundreds of years of high technological living; but there is an *entropy crisis*.

Not only the heat from our industrial processes, but also a thousand and one new chemicals cloud the air, ground and water, to interfere with the tightly woven and stable process of the earth organism.

By becoming independent of the solar drive chain we have been able to make any artefact we desire. Yet by the act of independence we have generated a disordered situation which is directly opposed to the natural currents of life on the planet.

But I have claimed that this book is an account of a revolution and revolutionary, so how is it that Gaia will detect and act against this breakaway behaviour? So far I have shown only that there is energy flow through the environment in the form of the solar drive chain, and that there are two basic laws which govern the conversion of that energy. This is a far cry from the statement that Gaia is an intelligent individual with a purpose.

3

The Face of Gaia

What are the mechanisms of the earth organism?

The words biosphere and ecosphere are often used to describe the total feltwork of living material covering the earth. But the concept has now been extended to include not only all the life-forms but the soil, the rocks, the oceans and the atmosphere. It is basic to the 'Gaia hypothesis' of Lovelock and his collaborators, that both living and non-living systems on the earth are combined to form the main anatomical framework of the earth organism, and that there is a fundamental link between the two. They believe that when life took hold on the planet, it did so not just because physical conditions were suitable, but by actively modifying the non-living environment. As life evolved, it modified its non-living environment. As life evolved, it modified its non-continuance. That is, life has an inbuilt pressure to survive and an ability to make changes. But before I develop this idea, I want to look at just one specialized subject. It is called *Cybernetics* and it will be a help in our study of the anatomy of Gaia.

Cybernetics is a name given to the study of self-regulating control systems. It is borrowed from an ancient myth about a character called Cybernetes who was the steersman of a boat ferrying the dead across the River Styx.

As he guided his silent cargo across the river, we can imagine a current turning the boat to the left. Cybernetes then moved the rudder to the right and corrected the error. Then he found that he had overcorrected and the boat veered to the right again. So, he moved the rudder to the left, but this time not so far and the boat finally straightened out on to its proper course. The old gentleman was a self-regulating control system, although he might not have appreciated the title. The system also tended towards stability: that is towards the goal of making the boat move steadily on course across the river.

Cybernetes has long since been replaced by an automatic machine which senses the desired course by compasses and other instruments, and keeps the boat on a straight course with a minimum of swings from left to right.

There are many other cases of self-regulation. A boiler heats radiators, the radiators reach the desired temperature, a thermostat senses that temperature and turns the boiler off. The temperature in the radiators gradually falls, the thermostat senses the fall and switches the boiler back on, and the radiators warm up again. This also is a self-stabilizing system maintaining the goal of a fixed temperature in the house. But the heating system has only one choice: to turn a switch on or off.

Now suppose that the heating system has been wrongly wired and that every time the radiators are hot, the boiler switches on, and if the radiators are cold, the boiler switches off. It is easy to see that the system is now unstable. Either the boiler goes on heating up and finally explodes or it shuts down altogether and remains cold.

Control systems of this sort are said to contain a 'feedback loop'. The correctly wired boiler system is called 'negative feedback' and the wrongly wired system is called 'positive feedback'.

Negative feedback is self-stabilizing and positive feedback leads to progressive instability and breakdown.

Cybernetes and the boiler were feedback systems with only one choice: to turn a rudder, or to operate a switch.

The human body contains a large number of interlinked feedback systems, and so it has multiple choice. An example, again used by Lovelock, is the control of body temperature. Heat sensors can make the body sweat, or shiver, or cause more or less blood to flow through the blood vessels of the skin like a radiator. The body is able to make a decision between a variety of choices.

So here is a basis for the anatomy of a goddess. The relationship between all the living and non-living parts of the earth organism is a complex of self-stabilizing systems with the inbuilt goal of keeping planetary conditions at an optimum for the maintenance of life. And the life-form of Gaia, without the intervention of man, is a sun-driven complex of multiple choice stabilizing systems, all of which tend to maintain stability and a balance between order and disorder.

But this is still a mechanistic description. Where is the revolutionary individual, where are the senses which recognize the need for action, where is the intelligence which exercises judgment and produces change? Where are the limbs and tools of Gaia?

We make a model of the outside world in our heads by using our senses. Light falls on the retina of the eye which writes a code about the picture and sends it to the brain, where the signals are decoded and assembled in a form which gives us our view of life outside our head. Is there an equivalent in Gaia? We also hold on tight to the belief that we have a will and a mind. Has Gaia the same?

There are a number of ways whereby life can modify the non-living world to make things better for itself. For example, the process of respiration releases carbon dioxide, which is one of the 'greenhouse gases' which tend to reflect heat escaping from the earth's surface back down on to the surface again. Evaporated water released from forests can modify cloud cover and the growth of algae on the surface of water can reduce evaporation. Even the reflectivity or 'albedo' of the planet is altered by the amount of green plants covering its surface. A dark surface absorbs more heat than a light one. So life can modify the non-living parts of the planet.

Millions of years before the first animals, the earth was teeming with the more primitive life-forms such as algae and bacteria, and Lovelock believes that these tiny life-forms produced a massive alteration in the composition and circulation of the elements of the planet – an alteration which is still continuing.

He also makes an ingenious comparison between Venus, Earth and Mars to show what the earth would have been like without the changes wrought by the life-forms. He gives details of gas concentrations in the atmospheres of our two planetary neighbours, and shows that the actual concentrations of gases in our own atmosphere differ by hundreds per cent from the values which would have been expected if life had not occurred. His conclusion is that life modifies the atmosphere as well.

The physical part of Gaia therefore is a sun-driven complex of living and non-living systems, which by a process of feedback control and in the absence of man maintains stability with little increase in disorder. Life modifies the non-living parts of the system towards the optimum conditions for the continued support of life.

But this description is still incomplete. A medical student dissects a human body and learns about the nervous, vascular and muscular systems it contains, and ends up with a blueprint for a human being. Yet this gives no insight into the feelings of love, creativity or anger which the living individual might have possessed. So, to persist with purely physical reductionist explanations of Gaia leads to the same error that has perpetuated the view that the whole is the sum of the parts.

There are no senses, muscles or nerves in Gaia in the human anatomical sense, but there are lines of communication and systems which act in a similar way. To see them involves a new attitude which denies the possibility that humans can stand apart from a situation and says instead that we can only be participating observers in a single whole.

Reductionist science is based on that of the ancient Greek civilization, which sought to account for the world of sense experience without having to involve a personal God. From these origins came the step personified by Galileo, who stated that sense experience must always be followed by demonstration, and finally, through the age of reason, came institutional science with its highly integrated control of cultural and intellectual freedom. Most recently 'critical science' has made its appearance, an approach which re-evaluates science in relation to social need and political imperatives.

Although critical science is a step beyond the intellectual corruption which follows from a science based upon money and state approval, it is still completely human-centred. It may seek to improve the human condition by criticizing those acts of science which are harmful to people, and this is valuable, but it gives no heed to the requirements of Gaia and makes no attempt to re-form the connection between man and the life process which is the key to a sustainable future. It still puts man first and the earth organism second.

Institutional science has a highly developed and mechanical view of reality, but *holistic* science, which is now beginning to emerge, takes a different view. It is opposed to the reductionist standpoint, which it holds to be inadequate, narrow and self-limiting to a point where only restricted and biased descriptions of reality emerge. It also questions the idea of 'objectivity' and proposes that there are alternative frameworks of reality and that these depend essentially on the attitudes and perceptions of the individual. It would support Sir James Jeans's famous statement that:

> The universe looks less and less like a great machine and more like a great thought.

It would also welcome Plato's lesson of the cave where shackled prisoners were shown only the shadows of things projected on the wall, outlined by the light of a fire. When the prisoners were released into the outside world, they believed that their surroundings were imaginary since their reality was made of shadows.

The proponents of the new science are at present a scattered and motley band, but if and when a more generally agreed discipline emerges among them, it will lead naturally to an understanding not only of the physical systems of the earth organism, but also to an understanding of its intelligence and its goals.

And yet, you may argue, we are *not* a part of any other creature or entity. We are obviously individuals, separate from Gaia. We have individual brains which direct the activities of individual physical bodies limited by skin. Beyond the skin, there is space and then beyond the space the skin of another individual and so on. We also believe that we have choice, free will and the capacity to act. We need to believe this view of things to get about the everyday world of tools and cities.

As a hesitant *Gaian*, if I may coin the word, I see individuality as a temporary separation from the fabric of the universal life process. Imagine a flexible sheet of infinite extent. All plants, animals and humans emerge from the sheet as if someone had pushed a finger against the reverse side and made it bulge. The bulge becomes a sphere with a thin neck still attached. Then the neck becomes almost infinitely thin and the now individual life in the sphere is born and free for just a lifetime. At death, the sphere contracts down on to the surface of the sheet, flattens and flows out again into the whole, until there is finally no trace of its previous existence. Imagine this process going on in both directions, millions and millions of times every second as the life process ebbs and flows between the separate and the conjugate. There is continuous change, motion and balance to produce stability and it is only we who imagine, falsely, that we are building a separate permanence.

But this is not to assume that our individuality began when we were born and finishes when we die, but rather that we are given a separate enclosure, a brief leasehold on a physically controllable entity for a short part of our total existence.

Here then is a clue to our relationship to the body of the earth organism. We assume, wrongly, that the thin neck of the sphere that connects us to the continuum is of no value and that we do not need to see down its extent. Yet this connection and its redevelopment is the main route to an expanded vision. By feeling our way back along the thread, we can find a new, or perhaps an old, vision of things which will expand our vision to a point where we can live a mutually symbiotic existence with Gaia.

By constantly training our minds to this vision we shall be able to appreciate the unified body of Gaia in an intuitive way which would make it impossible for us to act against the natural currents of her fabric.

But this step does involve a complete reassessment and probable refutation of our present high technological way of life.

To summarize so far: the physical structure of the earth organism, the body of the goddess, is a dynamic sun-driven network of interaction and control, composed of an uncountable number of stabilizing feedback loops, each of which interrelates with its neighbour. We humans were once an integral and functional part of this network, but have now separated ourselves from it in a way which is incompatible with our survival. Every organism, animal, fish and bird is a part of the organism, as are the rocks, the air, the ground and the oceans. The whole is held together by the flow of information which maintains overall stability, which tends to create conditions optimal for the continuance of the life process, but which tends to evolve conditions which are unfavourable to individual species that break the rules of the stable network. To justify this last statement, I now have to ask the question: has the body a mind?

4

The Mind of Gaia

The human mind is probably resident in the brain, and the brain is a mass of communicating pathways receiving data about the outside world via the senses, while also giving out commands to the body. Psychologists assert that the mind or the brain exhibits a quality called 'intelligence' and that this quality can be measured. Unfortunately, intelligence is probably the only quality which is measured with numbers in the complete absence of a generally acceptable definition of what is being measured. Clearly the word 'intelligence' has meaning, but its users tend to use human behaviour as a sole standard for its understanding, and even *The Oxford English Dictionary* stutters into tautology by defining it as 'intellect', 'understanding', 'sagacity', and 'quickness of understanding'. If you then look up the word 'sagacity', you find that it means 'exceptional intelligence'!

Psychologists devise what are called 'intelligence tests'. The IQ or intelligence quotient, for example, is believed to provide some indication of relative human ability: whereas all it can actually do is to demonstrate an ability to do well in an IQ test. Other tests are alleged to measure human qualities such as creativity and drive, all without any generally agreed definition of the quality under test.

A more irrational situation would be hard to imagine, but definitions still abound. The psychologist William Stern called intelligence 'the general capacity of an individual consciously to adjust his thinking to new requirements and a general adaptability to new problems and conditions'. Alfred Binet, the inventor of the 'intelligence test', thought the concept related to 'comprehension, invention, direction and criticism, or judgment'. And David Wechsler wrote that it is 'the aggregate or global capacity of an individual to act purposefully, to think rationally and to deal effectively with his environment'.

One wonders how Michelangelo, Beethoven or Dylan Thomas would have fared under such a blizzard of words.

Although these attempts at definition are anthropocentric in character, a relatively new study has now appeared called 'artificial intelligence',[1] whose proponents make machines which they believe act in an 'intelligent' fashion. Various quite sophisticated robots have been made, some of which have inbuilt goals, such as the need to seek light or the ability to produce language or primitive reasoning. Although the subject is part crippled by the logical problem that it is impossible to build an artificial version of something which cannot be defined, some of the 'definitions' of intelligence which have emerged are interesting in relation to the activities of the earth organism. One version is 'the ability of any decision-making entity to achieve a degree of success in seeking a wide variety of goals under a wide range of environments'.

This is a more general definition, that is not so human-centred as those I quoted earlier. 'Decision-making entity' could apply to a man or a machine or the thermostat of the boiler system, or indeed to the network of changes which go on in Gaia to maintain stability. 'A degree of success' simply means that a pre-defined goal tends to be achieved, and a 'wide range of environments' indicates adaptability.

It now seems possible to attempt a definition of the mind or brain of Gaia, and to say that it is an adaptable decision-making entity which tends to be successful in seeking the goal of the stability of the planetary life-form.

But animals, humans and goal-seeking machines all depend on senses for their evaluation of the surrounding world. Does Gaia also have an equivalent of senses?

I visited a scientist who works in the field of artificial intelligence. He had built a small robot and described it as a 'model of a blind man finding his way around a room'. It was a small covered box on three wheels. The 'room' was black tape

---

[1] *Artificial Intelligence through Simulated Evolution.* L. Fogel, A. Owens, M. Walsh. John Wiley & Sons, New York 1966.

set out in the form of a polygon on a flat silver board. Every time the robot approached the black tape surrounding it, it emitted a loud bleep. I suggested that the solution was apparently obvious. Underneath the robot there was a light sensor discriminating black tape from silver board. The scientist smiled wolfishly – he likes puzzles – and repeated the description of the model: it was of a *blind* man, so – no senses. Eventually the secret was revealed. Inside the robot there was a small model of the room and a sensor which 'felt' the walls of the model room. In other words, the robot had a *memory* of the outlines of the room and so needed no senses to find its way about.

So a blind man can find his way around a familiar room, partly by using the alternative senses of touch and sound and partly by memory. If no senses were available at all, if his hands were heavily gloved and ears blocked and other senses inactive, he could still find his way about from memory. Action can occur by reference to memory and without senses if information is present in a memory.

In the molecules and atoms of Gaia, there is just such a repository of stored information, which has been built up over the millennia by the constant need for stability and the need to modify the non-living parts of the planet to achieve optimum conditions for life.

I do not mean that somewhere hidden away in the earth there is a single brain or mind – just that there is stored information connected to points of action. It may be in a leaf, a molecule, an animal, or in the network of communication between all three. Just as Jung proposed basic archetypes behind the symbols and archetypal ideas of man, so is there an archetypal framework of information locked away in the fabric of the life-form, which we perhaps see only in the mind's eye, dimly.

Jung describes what he meant by an archetype:

It is, in my view, a great mistake to suppose that the psyche of a newborn child is a *tabula rasa* in the sense that there is nothing in it. In so far as a child is born with a differentiated brain that is predetermined by heredity and therefore individualized, it meets sensory stimuli coming from outside not with *any* aptitudes but with *specific* ones and this necessarily results in a particular, individual choice and pattern of apperception ... They are the archetypes which direct all fantasy activity into its appointed paths ... It is not therefore a question of inherited *ideas* but inherited possibilities of ideas.

Jung concluded that the archetypes originated with the origin of life itself, and were knowable only through the archetypal ideas and symbols they produced in man.

The mind of Gaia is similar by analogy. With the onset of life there came the capacity to store and generate 'archetypes of stability'. These are stored in the fabric of all living things and constantly reinforced by the collective experience of the life process itself. Again by analogy with Jung, the archetypes of stability which have developed in the substance of Gaia over the millennia are not themselves knowable, except by the effects they produce on the structure and behaviour of the various living and non-living parts of her body.

Can information, then, travel between yeast cells, fishes, birds and man? Is there a secret code flashing along all the physical pathways of the earth organism?

The cells of yeast, the molecules and atoms which make it up, are continually changing into other forms. Each cell either consumes or is consumed and dies and decays, so that its constituent atoms are eventually recycled into another life-form. Within the magnificent dynamic of the earth organism there is a constant ebb and flow of matter and energy. Nothing is ever still. The authors of one of the world's oldest books, the *I Ching*, were expressing a physical truth when they proposed that the essence of life is in the changes themselves. 'Life' is not in the amoeba as it slides over the surface of another organism, it is in the dynamic of the movement itself, in the relationship between the two creatures and in the eventual incorporation of one by the other. The archetypes of stability are not fixed matrices locked into the structures of a single creature or rock, but are constantly regenerated and maintained in the flow of matter and energy in Gaia. The flow of information, then, is not a secret code *between* organisms: it is in the process of change itself.

By now it would seem that I have sailed close to a restatement of Pantheism: a frequently recurring theme in ancient religion and philosophy, based upon the idea that everything is one and the one is God.

In ancient Greece, for example, nature was described as universally permeated with a divine substance; and the Indian vedantic philosophers posited the single infinite reality of 'Brahman' against the multi-faceted world of material objects.

In Europe, the concept waxed and waned through the centuries. Spinoza is the best-known pantheist and he was driven by the need to find the source of an independent good. Others adopted their own metaphor. Goethe wanted to reconcile pagan attitudes to nature, using the redemptive value systems of Christianity; and Hegel wrote of an 'absolute ideal' which would take form only at the end of history, in a society which was fully self-conscious.

Goethe perhaps had a vision of the failure of pure reason as a means of understanding nature. His Mephistopheles is talking to the stricken Faust:

> The scholars are everywhere believers,
> But never succeed in being weavers,
> He who would study organic existence,
> First draws out the soul with rigid persistence;
> The parts he may hold in his hand he may hold and class
> But the spiritual link is lost, alas!

A spiritual link. So is Gaia immanent in God or is God in Gaia? Is the idea of Gaia another restatement of Pantheism?

Gaia is an entity originating from the archetype of the earth organism, and as a 'Gaian' science emerges it may become possible to look beyond the archetype, to follow the dynamic of the earth organism and to see greatly extended images of the universe. The current picture of a fully analysed and random universe is a monotone and drear landscape which shows no sign of evolution. There is pattern, order, intelligence and beauty to be found in the fabric of Gaia if we can learn to see clearly enough, and if we can learn or relearn the ability to look down the thin cord connecting our spheres of individuality to the infinite surface of life. So the concept of Gaia is perhaps a myth for a post-industrial age rather than Pantheism restated.

To reach beyond the fetters of reductionism and to look outwards at the whole, is to be overcome by a blinding series of beautiful discoveries. Once the shock of the brilliance wears off, vision is cleared absolutely. It is possible to see, for the first time, that instead of the grammes and molecules and the symbols of mathematics, there exists a colossal dynamic of change, action and counter-action. But to view nature in this way is *not* to dispense with reason or discipline. It is just an introductory process which leads naturally to an extension of the senses. Holism must follow the admission of failure of reductionism; it cannot replace it, for if that were to happen we would be at the mercy of the cults of unreason. It is not *reason* which should be avoided, but the *tyranny* of reason.

So, given this concept of Gaian intelligence, is it possible for the toymakers, with their powerful machines, to destroy Gaia? The answer given by the toymakers is often cloaked in assertions of power: 'man has now grown so powerful that he is capable of destroying life on earth altogether'; or, 'the atomic age could reduce the globe to ashes'. It seems they take a terrible pride in dangerous machines.

What are Gaia's defences? How does she take her revenge? We now know enough to recognize that, even if the hubris of the toymakers releases the ultimate pollutant, if it causes the last nuclear war to be fought, long after we have sunk without trace into our own chemical ooze, somewhere in a dark, wet crevice in a rock, spores of bacteria and algae will be waiting, ready to start the whole cycle over again once the clouds of poison have drifted away into space. We will never have the power to destroy Gaia. Even if we succeed in ablating the last bacterium, the motes of life are already hanging in space, waiting to coalesce, waiting to start again. It will just take time; time which we would not perceive.

To look at the length of our high technology age and compare it with the extent of our history as a species, it is a shock to discover that technical man is a very recent phenomenon. Although we have walked upright on the earth for more than three million years, our present technology started to burgeon only a few hundred years ago. If one day, from midnight to midnight, is made equivalent to our 3 million year history, then our present technology began at about five seconds before midnight. In one fifteen thousandth of our total time on the earth we have managed to inflict permanent damage on our planet.

But Gaia's long-term perspective is not her only defence against the hubris of technological man.

Earlier, I mentioned cybernetics, and the negative feedback loops which tend to produce stability. I used boiler thermostats and the control of body temperature as examples of negative feedback systems, the first with only a single choice and the second with multiple choice. Now the switch of the thermostat operates, say, in a tenth of a second, but to alter and stabilize the body temperature may take several minutes. So feedback systems can take different times to go through their full cycle of operation: the boiler thermostat is said to have a relatively *short cycle time* and the body temperature control system a *longer cycle time*.

There are millions of interwoven feedback loops in Gaia, with enormously variable cycle times. Some may cycle in hours, others may take centuries. We have, I believe, ignored the long cycle time loops because they are not foreseeable in a lifetime. This has given us a false confidence, since it makes our accelerating technologies seem only to do local tactical damage.

Each new process with its inevitable trail of entropy breaks the relatively short cycle times of Gaia's stabilizing loops, and as we refashion the atoms and molecules of her substance into hardware, we assume that our processes of control are wholly successful and have given rise to no overall planetary deficit. But quite apart from the growing increase in entropy or disorder, there are negative feedback loops of a much longer cycle time in operation.

The life process has a long-term elasticity and can ride with the blows of technical man until a certain strain is reached, then it rebounds with accelerating speed to restore stability.

A good example of a long cycle-time feedback loop in which repair information flows between primitive creatures is the relatively recent appearance of what is called *transferable drug resistance* in bacteria.

Antibiotics are chemicals, derived from living bacteria or moulds, which can kill other bacteria. They are used to control infectious diseases in man and animals, to control diseases in food crops, to stimulate the growth of animals and to preserve foods. Almost as soon as antibiotics were first used against 'pathogens', or disease-carrying bacteria, some strains of organism began to adapt and show resistance to them. Consequently, larger and larger doses of antibiotic had to be given to be effective. Resistance was first transferred from generation to generation of bacteria by ordinary mutation, and then by the transfer of genetic material from one cell to another by bacteriophages and viruses which infect bacteria.

For a while it looked as though this situation was containable by the development of new antibiotics, since ordinary resistance remained at a tolerable level. But then a further and quite sudden escalation of resistance occurred, called *transferable drug resistance*, which turned out to be a small masterpiece of molecular warfare.

This process is quite distinct from ordinary drug resistance. Bacteria had learned a more efficient adaptation mechanism: microscopic creatures with no sense, brain or nervous system had learned to communicate and to exchange information about a man-made danger to their survival.

In 1959 two Japanese scientists found that a strain of bacteria could quite suddenly become resistant to several antibiotics at once, and were able to *transfer* the resistance to members of different strains simply by cell-to-cell contact. Since then, this effect has been found on a worldwide basis and is accelerating. It involves the joining together of genetic material from one cell with that of another, and can happen between organisms of widely different type and between pathogens and non-pathogens.

Bacteria can pass information about resistance to others in small packets called *plasmids*. The life process first detects a threatening imbalance, and then designs and develops an effective way of restoring balance and removing the threat, by the use of a genetic language just as precise and versatile as the human spoken word.

This repair action by bacteria in a 'learning' situation is just as 'intelligent' and purposeful as that of a person who ducks when someone throws a brick. But it also has an *offensive* capability far beyond the mere avoidance involved in ducking a brick.

In 1963, a small creature with a large Latin name, *Myzus persicae*, was totally susceptible to insecticide sprays. By 1976 some collected samples showed 80–100 per cent resistance to the same chemicals. This tiny Aphid had 'learnt' how to make an enzyme which broke molecular links in the insecticide, thus rendering it ineffective, and it is now showing signs of extending this newly intelligent capability to cover other new and more complex chemicals. The really important result of this adaptation is that if a mixed population of resistant and non-resistant Aphids are sprayed, the non-resistant are killed and the resistant survive. This means that the resistant strains are left to multiply and so the 'Super-Aphid' is triumphantly more numerous. This illustrates an important underlying principle of the purposive, intelligent action of the earth organism: *to turn offence into advantage*. A danger is presented, the danger is overcome and those who overcome the danger become selectively more numerous. It is not just that the fittest survive, but that the offence *itself* causes the survivors to become more numerous.

The more we oppose the natural currents of the earth organism, the more opposition is developed in a proportion which renders any final success on the part of the toymakers utterly impossible. Nowhere has there ever been an attack in war which had as its final conclusion the creation of more enemy troops. As I write, the earth organism is in a tumult of revolt. Sixty-seven swarms of desert locust are ravaging the Horn of Africa. There are now 150 grasshoppers to the square yard in eastern Colorado. The gypsy moth is burgeoning in the north-east of the United States, the fire ant in the south-east and the corn borer in the mid-west. Insects and pests which were, until recently, well under chemical control are now rushing back in unprecedented numbers.

The United States Agency for International Development now states that: 'Malaria is rapidly becoming a major disease in parts of the world that have not been troubled by it for 20 years, and is now on its way to becoming a major international problem.' The Anopheline mosquito, once so confidently suppressed by the proponents of DDT, has now returned but with new 'intelligence' and new 'knowledge' about man's chemical attack. During this year there were almost 200 million new cases of malaria resulting in the estimated death of one million children in Africa alone.

DDT has now been replaced by BHC or benzene hexachloride and already 43 separate species of mosquito have learnt immunity to it. And the malarial parasite itself which causes the disease is showing a widespread resistance to anti-malarial drugs. In 1952 India had reduced the incidence of malaria from 10 million to 60,000; by 1976 the number of cases had risen again to 6 million. Man's offence had been truly turned into advantage. Each shot fired by the toymakers comes back a hundredfold.

Each single individual living organism has no choice but to follow the natural currents of this great flowing dynamic and so generate no offence against the whole. But our activities work strategically against these currents, and each time we create new technology, not only do we oppose the currents but we actually sever the stable links between the myriad ecosystems. It is not that the earth organism copes with our attack, but that the attack leads to a strengthening of its resources. Among the archetypes of stability there is a learnt increase in stored data about possible sources of danger. Just as the immune systems of the human body learn specific protective blueprints about specific disease organisms, so does the earth organism memorize specific threats to its stability – but with the added quality of evolving with the experience.

The trap lies in believing that because nature *does* appear to ride with the blow, none of the self-protective mechanisms of the earth organism which I have been describing is at all dangerous. We forget that the cycle time of some feedback loops may take generations to complete.

That there is a pressure to survive behind the life process is obvious. What the pressure is no scientist has the slightest idea, but it is there for all to see.

The mind of Gaia is in a permanent state of evolution and a permanent state of revolution, in the sense that it is continually transforming its own structure to maintain conditions at an optimum for the continuance of the life process.

It is not, 'if you can't beat them join them', but: 'we have to join them in order to survive'.

Most of the processes of high technology aim at dominance and manipulation of the life process, but they can be consistent only with a short-term future, since intelligently driven stabilizing forces like the 'conversing' bacteria are gathering information for the necessary adaptation or repair action. It is clear that we are capable of almost any act of control or alteration. We can certainly divert rivers and cleave the atom. We can change whole species until they suit our needs. We are able to destroy whole populations of animals and humans and we can modify entire landscapes with giant machines.

We can also sidestep whatever evolutionary process has been at work in Gaia and act in a truly independent way. But *only for a short time*. The biologist J. Z. Young has referred to an 'extra genetic stream of evolution which is called knowledge'.[2] We have repositories of skills, tools and engines to do almost anything a rich group of people decide to do. The Apollo moonshot was the end result of a consensus between industrialists, governmental officials and the military to bring together bodies of knowledge and groups of specialists which would eventually result in the placement of humans on the surface of the moon. No new scientific knowledge had to be sought; it was just a matter of good tool design and the tool was the spaceship.

There are as many different ways of looking at a problem as there are people, and I have been making the case for an intelligent, decision-making, goal-seeking entity called Gaia: an entity with a built-in pressure to survive and a need to establish a low-entropy and stable planetary situation where each of its myriad of single living organisms can flourish.

A biologist would look at the situation from the point of view of cells, tissues and organs; a biochemist in terms of metabolic systems; and a physicist would measure temperatures and pressures.

But one science stands out as different from the others because it deals only with interrelationships; it is called Ecology. The name was derived by Haeckel from the Greek words for 'dwelling place' and 'study': *Oikos* and *logos*. *Oikologos* became 'ecology', and it will be helpful to look at some of its basic ideas, because

[2] *An Introduction to the Study of Man*. J. Z. Young, RRS, 1977.

through them, an understanding of the opposing revolutionary force of Gaia can be gained. So far I have been depicting only an intelligent entity with the power to take adaptive action, not one which can attack.

5

Ecology and the Intelligent Goddess

The reductionist sciences render systems down to their parts, but ecology explores the relationships between the species and between species and environment. As Garrett Hardin half-seriously put it, ecology 'connects everything to everything else'. Ecology studies the relationship between man, animals and environment.

Ecologists talk about basic groups: organisms, populations, communities, ecosystems, environments and the ecosphere (Fig. 4).

> A tree is an organism.
> A man is an organism.
> A lion is an organism.
> A cabbage is an organism.
> A bacterium is an organism.

Organisms grouped together become populations.

> A forest of trees is a population.
> A tribe of people is a population.
> A pride of lions is a population.
> A field of cabbages is a population.
> A culture of bacteria is a population.

Populations of various organisms can be found in one place at one time. They interrelate. Interrelated populations of various organisms are called a community.

> A tribe and its farmland is a community.
> A man and his garden is a community.
> The population and farmland of a country is a community.
> The inhabitants of a city are *not* a community.

The Community of
the Life Process

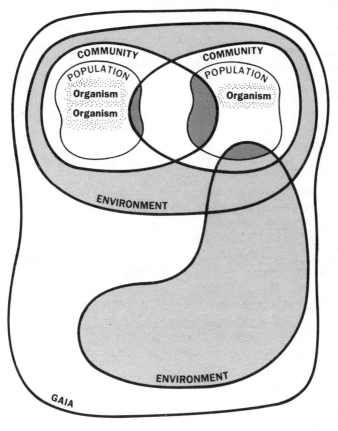

Figure 4

A community must have a place on the earth to live. The place is called an environment.

An environment is made of the earth, the sky and the water. It is driven by the energy of the sun, the power of the wind, the warmth of the ground.

A population of organisms living as a community in an environment, is called an ecosystem.

> A tropical island is an ecosystem.
> A lake is an ecosystem.
> A forest is an ecosystem.
> A rock pool is an ecosystem.

All the ecosystems together form the ecosphere. The ecosphere is also called the biosphere, and the amount of living material in the biosphere is called the biomass.

There are an uncountable number of ecosystems and they are all interconnected. I am simply extending this idea when I say that the connections are the nervous system of Gaia, that the information which travels along the connections between the systems is the intelligence of Gaia, and that the Gaian archetypes are stored in these connections. The Gaian archetypes I visualize as the diffuse memory of survival and stability learned by the constantly experimental process of evolution. In the connections resides the non-human intelligence of Gaia, which maintains the life process and modifies the processes of the planet to achieve stability. Through a planet-wide myriad of eyes and senses, through the movements, feeding patterns and replication of an uncountable number of species, by means of drought, storm, pestilence and the deployment of solar energy, the life process and the non-living planet are linked in an awesome dynamic of stability.

We have already seen that Gaia is able to change the reflectivity of the earth, modify the atmosphere and alter the flow of materials to maintain stability and to optimize conditions to suit life. A smaller part of the organism, an ecosystem, can do the same.

An ecosystem acts in a similar way on a smaller scale, first by modifying the rate of cycling of chemicals through its systems and then by regulating the flow of energy. Our planet is almost a closed system which takes on or loses practically no matter. Some fragments of rock from large volcanoes may have been expelled with such force as to go flying into orbit in space, and meteorites from space do strike the earth, adding minutely to its total mass; but for all intents and purposes the earth does not change in mass or content. This means that the earth organism has to recycle all its material constituents within that system. There is no doorstep delivery of fresh material. Water, oxygen, nitrogen, phosphorus and carbon have all to be driven around closed loops and conserved on a continuously recycled basis.

But the flow of energy from the sun through the living and non-living systems of the earth, which I have called *the solar drive chain*, is a one-way process. The rate of this flow is under the control of the life process in an ecosystem. Energy is packaged and distributed by the interrelationship of its organisms, such as in the connection between a predator and its prey. One good example of this was recorded a long time ago by men who knew nothing of science.

The employees of the Hudson's Bay Company in the north of Canada were interested in the number of fox skins they took from trappers each year. They found, after keeping records for some years, that there was a fluctuating change in the number of skins taken every three or four years. Then they discovered that this variation was tied to the size of the lemming population. The lemmings, which the fox eats, have a very high birth-rate for short periods, then they die off leaving only a few survivors who take three or four years to re-establish their former numbers. Then the trappers found that the snowy owl also had a similar population frequency of three to four years, and also fed on lemmings.

Population sizes in an ecosystem are closely interdependent. This is another way of saying that energy flow in an ecosystem is controlled by its species. Looking at Figure 5, the chain of events starting from the incoming energy from the sun is under the part control of each individual population of organisms. For example, if climate conditions were to affect a particular population of plants and they died off, the energy contained in their substance would be short-circuited directly to the decay process without first going into primary and then secondary consumers.

Our present culture indoctrinates people with the idea that decay is horrible and smelly. But it is an essential part of the natural cycle of events, and the disposal methods of high technology break this entirely. Our sewage, for example, is swept out to sea to poison the sea bed, instead of going back into the soil to make nutrients for plants. A slogan for a Gaian future might therefore be: *Decay is beautiful.*

Most of our actions are directly opposed to these cyclical processes within Gaia, and Figure 6 shows the general layout of this opposition.

The boiler thermostat is a stable negative feedback loop with a single choice. The heat regulation system of the body is a stable negative feedback loop with multiple choice, and it is a general rule of cybernetics that the more choices of operation a self-stabilizing system has, the more effective and the more resilient to damage it is likely to be.

If the thermostat fails, the boiler heating system stops, but if the shivering mechanism of the body fails, heat loss or gain can still be achieved by regulating either the flow of blood through skin blood vessels, or the amount of sweat released. By analogy, stability within Gaia, or within one of her parts such as an ecosystem, is partly maintained by species diversity.

Suppose now that there has been a nuclear war and that the last great technological convulsion has destroyed the human race, and wiped away much of the ecosphere leaving a scorched planet. Would the last Wagnerian dream of the toymakers have been realized? Would Gaia be dead as well? The answer is a clear no. We could perhaps push the flow of the organism back for a long time – a century perhaps – but the pressure of the earth organism to live, to interrelate and to re-establish itself would still be there.

How do we know this?

In 1883, a violent volcanic explosion devastated the island of Krakatoa. Several cubic miles of rock were blown into the air with sufficient violence to inject dust into orbit around the world; dust which coloured sunsets for years.

With a force equal to approximately six large hydrogen bomb

Life & Decay

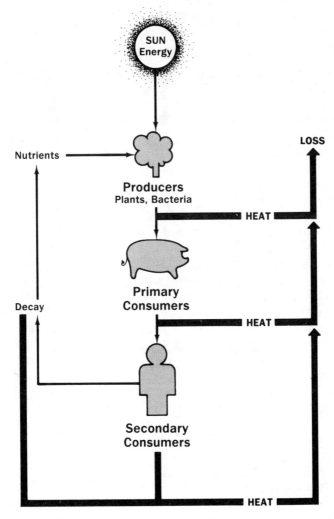

Figure 5

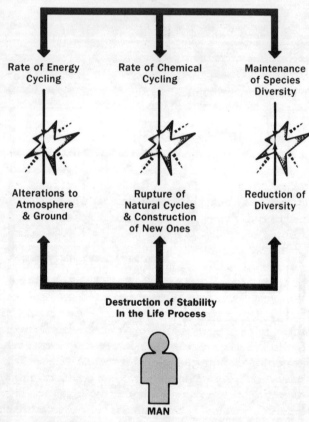

GAIA
Control of Stability
in the Life Process

Rate of Energy
Cycling

Rate of Chemical
Cycling

Maintenance
of Species
Diversity

Alterations to
Atmosphere
& Ground

Rupture of
Natural Cycles
& Construction
of New Ones

Reduction of
Diversity

**Destruction of Stability
In the Life Process**

MAN

Figure 6

explosions, one whole island was burnt clean of any life, except possibly for a few lowly organisms in crevices and caves: a naturally occurring nuclear war. The tide of the earth organism was violently pushed back.

Nine months later, a single spider was found laboriously fabricating its web.

Three years later, eleven species of fern and eleven flowering plants had reappeared.

In about ten years, the ravaged island was once again covered by a green pelt of life. Coconut trees had re-established themselves, orchids were flowering, shrubs were prospering and creepers were extending their feelers into the new jungle.

Twenty years after the fire of the volcano, there were birds, snails, rodents and reptiles; altogether 250 different species of animals.

At present, over ninety years after the Armageddon of the volcano, there are dense forests, 52 vertebrate species and the full pulsing rhythm of life. But even now ecologists believe that the full stabilizing process of Krakatoa is not yet complete. The integrated, intelligent pressure of Gaia to survive has not yet reached its end.

Krakatoa was fully 25 miles from the nearest island, the nearest repository of life, and yet the whole process was brought back to the island, by coconuts floating on the tide, by birds carrying seeds and insects and by dust flowing on the wind.

Such is Gaia's recuperative power. But what can we now conclude about the nature of the revolutionary action of Gaia?

Earlier, I described the acquisition of insecticide resistance by the Super-Aphids as an example of intelligent adaptation, and suggested that the subsequent increase in numbers of the resistant strains was an example of the earth organism turning *offence into advantage*. Man develops an insecticide which has only one end result: it produces a larger number of creatures which the insecticide cannot destroy. And this is not a 'draw' situation for man, but an actual 'loss' since the earth organism has increased its capability to withstand attack. The principle is similar to that of the martial art of Judo, wherein the attacker is thrown by the momentum of his own aggression.

The revolutionary action of the earth organism then is to

transform itself continually by converting *threat into advantage* and *damage into evolution*.

Amid the almost infinite variety and number of feedback loops, and the endless sequences of information coursing along the interconnections, there is an apparently inexhaustible ability, not only to 'ride with the blow' of an offender, but to burgeon and evolve as a direct result of the blow.

In this part of the book I have tried to show that the industrial society completely opposes the aims and objectives of a planet-wide individual entity with purpose, intelligence and the ability to change. I have also suggested that although it is impossible for us to oppose the natural currents and imperatives of this individual, it *is* possible to understand the way these natural currents work and therefore to plan a way of life which is in accord with them. The industrial society, with its lethal output of entropy, I have shown to be directly opposed to them. So it follows that the industrial society must be abandoned.

The second part of this book is an investigation into certain personal changes which I have made and others can make, to effect a partial separation of the individual from the industrial society. In the space of one book, I have been able only to make basic suggestions about attitudes and the details of day-to-day living. I hope that it will stimulate others to be more detailed about particular aspects of it.

PART TWO

Change and Refutation

6

To Break a Habit

Nothing is complete or perfect. I am writing with a machine-made propelling pencil on machine-made paper. My scribble will be typed with a machine-made typewriter and this book will be printed on large machine presses.

But before getting down to the nuts-and-bolts changes in everyday activity, I want to look first at the massive conditioning process which keeps the *consumer syndrome* running.

The toymakers have studied, measured and recorded every phase of the despoliation of the earth, and yet they still design processes which they know will accelerate despoliation. No one put the situation with greater acerbity than Bertolt Brecht:

> Out of the libraries stride the slaughterers,
> Mothers gaze numbly at the skies
> for the inventions of the scholars.

The technologists make use of a scientific method which has produced an obvious profusion of discovery. So I am not proposing that its processes of logic and experiment are inherently faulty: only that it has been exploited in isolation, to develop a body of knowledge which is fundamentally incomplete. Such an approach does not consider anything other than logical analysis, and fails to include all that is most humane and poetic in man as a part of its structure. It excludes altogether any basic respect or love for the universe, it rejects the inclusion of the sensations of beauty and feeling, and treats with derision anyone who holds a love and respect for natural things.

The toymakers are devoted to systems of control, and have, in consequence, become dehumanized advocates of the domination of nature. They have codified a view of nature which suppresses the most essential features about survival and about our relationship to the life process. Above all, they have trained us to believe that there is nature, and there is man. But man *is* nature. Just as an organism is in a population, a population is in a community, the community is in an environment and the environment is in a planet, *so are we in Gaia*. There is no possibility that we ever *could* separate ourselves. Yet the toymakers have *imagined* that we could, and have distorted the truth sufficiently to ensure that this belief is welded firmly into our culture.

For example, we are conditioned to believe that 'energy' is a basic problem, and that once enough 'energy' is generated, our problems will be over. It is already part of our current belief system that there is an 'energy crisis' and that by the development of new techniques of nuclear fission and fusion, the energy crisis will be solved. But this is no more than a conditioning myth to make people focus on one problem while they are told that the solution is just around the corner. The heroes of technology have simply been given a new task. The facts of entropy are ignored. I have already shown that there is no such thing as an energy crisis: the name was invented to provide further justification for the ingenuity of the toymakers.

No further problems of existence on this planet can be solved by technological process alone. We shall always be offered what is called the 'technological fix' to solve our problems, and the fix will always fail because of the inescapable problem of entropy. There is oil and coal to burn for centuries to come, but to do so would cloak the planet in a lethal miasma of disorder.

We have therefore to look for a way of life which could break what some ecologists are already beginning to call the 'entropic trap'. This must involve a complete re-examination of each and every aspect of life, for every aspect of our lives is involved. And it will not be possible to obey the rules of logical analysis alone, because these can lead only to yet another reductionist view of nature, based on yet another analysis, another taxonomy and another body of knowledge with no value system built into it.

The materialist analysis looks complete at first sight. But do we really accept that the universe is made of matter and energy alone? Or that the human body and its beautifully integrated systems, its absolute and complete suitability for the purpose of its occupant, was the result of blind unintelligent groping by a random evolutionary system?

The toymakers assert that the creative profusion of the human brain is the direct result of a developmental process which has proceeded in a steady linear direction from the first life-forms. They claim that the paintings of Leonardo da Vinci were the direct result of the fittest surviving and of spontaneous gene mutation! Or Beethoven's ninth symphony, to celebrate Schiller's poem of joy, was a function of his relationship to his ancestral amoebae! Or the Alhambra was the product of mere 'intelligent vertebrate descendants of the primate'.

We have the priceless gifts of language, self-awareness and vision. With these we can see beyond the bare necessities of food, warmth and shelter, and yet we have consciously, with both intelligence and premeditation, decided to pursue a course which we know perfectly well will destroy us.[1] It therefore follows that we are consciously committing a protracted suicide.

We have all the necessary evidence to decide between an infinitely renewable future and a quick, corrosive death. Our stockpiles of information are complete. We know how to survive and yet we choose death for ourselves and no chance of a full life-span for our children.

It is as if we are standing in front of a copper bar labelled 'danger high voltage', and we deliberately and with full premeditation reach forward to touch it with bare hands. Why do we have this astonishing death wish? I believe that it may stem partly from a subconscious realization that our present way of life is not only despoliating but also devoid of inner reward. The glitter of the motor car and the washing machine and the blandishments of television are all intended as reward symbols of success and gratification. They were developed to ease day-to-day life and to provide convenience, but now washing machines stand idle in droughts and ninety-miles-per-hour cars stand motionless in columns on the motorways. There is a subconscious realization that however much these ephemeral symbols were improved they would never generate any inward

[1] In the fourth century, a philosopher, Ko Fung, wrote: 'As for belief there are things that are as clear as the sky and yet men prefer to sit under an upturned barrel.'

happiness or a real sense of ease. They are symbols of despair and failure: surrogates for achievement, which encourage us to live on the outside of our senses and actually diminish the quality of life.

Simultaneously, we are realizing very clearly that these artefacts are directly related to exploding chemical plants and poisoned land; and that not only has the dream of a technological nirvana vanished, but that it is producing a burgeoning series of consequences which are both ugly and frightening. Each time we buy another nylon article in a shop, we know perfectly well that we have acquired more shares in the explosions and death at Flixborough or its inevitable successor.

Entirely undemocratic bureaucracies have evolved, and secretive and uneasy bargains are struck between governments and manufacturers, to patch up this manifestly failing system. Desperate men still try to hold the industrial machine together, although we have already been flung into the first years of the post-industrial society.

The evolution of a post-industrial way of life is going to be uniquely difficult because of this powerful conditioning to which we have all been subjected. It can only be achieved by progressive individual separation from the processes of industrial-technical society. Yet the very idea seems absurd, particularly to someone who is working forty hours a week in the dehumanizing bedlam of a production line, and clearly needs to use leisure time simply to recover from the experience. It is ironic perhaps that the change can only first be attempted by relatively affluent people such as myself. I do not have to work on a production line and have enough time to think and to write.

Further, to separate ordinary life from high technology will certainly not be risk-free. I have already referred to the member of a commune, leading a 'natural' and self-sufficient life in the country, who takes an antibiotic to cure an illness, and thus confirms his parasitic relationship with industrial society. Gaians, on the other hand, will have almost completely to deny themselves such drugs. Obviously in the first years of such a separate existence, sick people would still have to take antibiotics if life itself were threatened, but as time goes on, their bodies and those of their children would gradually reacquire the natural immunities which the age of antibiotics has manifestly destroyed. Thus there would be a definite, initial risk of increased suffering. I have expanded this assertion in the section on health.

We have been encouraged to believe that technology can provide. Water emerges continuously from the tap, electricity flows from the pattern of holes in the wall. But the truth is that, behind the tap and the holes in the wall, the first lethal miasmas of entropy are already fingering their way into our living space. We have the choice of starting to take risks now, or exposing ourselves to the terminal risk of the entropy crisis and the intelligent revolution of the earth organism.

Earlier on I mentioned the recolonization of Krakatoa by Gaia. Near where I live, it has happened on a smaller scale.

There is a ruined cottage in a field. It has been unoccupied for a century. Slowly, over the years, the weather has shaken its frame and broken the roof. Bacteria, lichens and animals have invaded the structure. Fungi have dissolved the wood, heat and cold chip the bricks and tiles. Creepers have forced their tendrils in along the sagging floorboards. Walls have crumbled. As the years pass, it looks less and less like a home and more and more like a pile of naturally growing life. The hard-sawn outlines of human labour have blurred into the outlines of leaves piling up in the wind. The plaster has powdered and earth accretes around the edges. The life processes, once so confidently pushed aside by the masons and the joiners, have flowed back to engulf the structure entirely, to take back their own.

To reconcile ourselves with this process, rather than make war with it, is the most *exciting* possibility in the changes I am proposing. They will enable us to live *with* this pressure of the earth organism. And there we shall find a basis for a new ideology and new levels of consciousness. By ideology I mean a new science of ideas, not another authoritarian analysis of the human condition. I do not believe that the changes are anything to do with any current political ideology: neither Marxists nor capitalists have the necessary ideas, and Maoists seem only a little less wedded to economic growth and control of the masses than the rest. Economists can only speak of growth, money, markets and profit.

Any ideology relevant to a sustainable future must originate from the prime survival need of living with Gaia. It cannot come from another analysis of the human condition by itself. All previous ideologies have been anthropocentric in this way and have made no allowance for the fact that we have to put our needs second to those of the earth organism. They have proposed instead that freedom, equality and brotherhood would automatically occur if the analysis of the human condition alone was carried out with sufficient care. But not only has history proved this to be wrong: there has been no recent attempt at all to evolve a vision of life based upon the broader issues which I have been trying to propose. Isolated political ideologies are abstractions which are based on ideas of human control and dominance.

If a post-industrial or *Gaian* way of life does develop, I believe that our present suicidal progress will not only disappear, but will be replaced by a profound advance in levels of awareness and happiness.

The basic principle behind the life of a Gaian is perfectly simple: to put the needs of man second to the needs of the earth organism. What follows now is a detailed analysis of changes to assist the achievement of this principle.

7

Change and Transformation

The industrial process has penetrated every aspect of our lives, so it is impossible in one book to provide a masterplan for a complete rejection of all its artefacts and processes. What I have done is to keep to basic needs, and to see how far these can be met by alternative methods. To survive we need:

1. Food and water.
2. Warmth.
3. Shelter.

To survive comfortably we also need:

4. Health.
5. Energy.
6. Tools.
7. Machines.

To survive comfortably within the limits set by the currents of Gaia, we need:

1. To develop a minimum entropy way of life.
2. To move consumption as far up the solar drive chain as possible.
3. To re-create a dependence on the solar drive chain, and to reject the use of fossil fuels as far as possible.
4. To restore the interrelationship between ourselves and the earth organism, and to reject any ideologies which propose dominance over it.
5. To evolve a science which has as its basic premise that we can only exist as an integral part of the earth organism.

To return for a moment to ecology. A person is an organism in a population of organisms, a population of organisms lives in an environment and all together make up the ecosphere. The problem about this way of looking at things, apart from people being called organisms and not people, is that the edges or boundaries of each part of the ecosphere overlap. Like the picture in Figure 4, one organism or person may live in the environment of another community and two communities may share the same territory. To make this clearer, and to create an image which relates us to what we do outside our skin, I am going to use the ideas of a *boundary* and a *system*.

A boundary is an imaginary line drawn around a something, and a system is anything going on inside the something.

So, a person is a system, a machine is a system and a group of people, large or small, is a system. This is just a way of thinking which defines limits and is not intended to minimize the importance of being human.

A boundary separates what is inside it from the outside world. It is an image I have borrowed from thermodynamics, and it is useful not because people are either thermodynamics or systems, but because it makes an easy visual model of our relationship with the surroundings: an imaginary stockade from which to peer out with new eyes.

Suppose that a rich man dislikes the surrounding world. He buys a house in the country and becomes a recluse. He stocks it with enough food and water to last for his entire life. He stores all his other worldly needs in the home and never again stirs outside.

If the man's house was perfectly insulated and contained all its own energy and oxygen generating systems; if it was not connected to main drains and if it put out no carbon dioxide and no garbage for collection; and if the man was his own doctor when sick, then we could say his existence was 'self-sufficient', and he would be a successful recluse. We could then draw his boundary round the external surface of the house.

But if, on the other hand, he travels outside the house only occasionally, then his boundary grows with his direction of travel like a bubble growing a finger. So a boundary is not always just a circle around a system, but it can extend according to movements of parts in the system.

A thermodynamicist would say that the man and his house

was a 'closed system' in that nothing travelled either way through his boundary. The thermodynamicist would contrast his situation with an 'open system', where some things, such as energy or matter, do travel across the boundary both ways.

In practice, all the man would need would be a machine gun, some barbed wire and a resident psychiatrist.

Self-sufficiency is now a much over-used concept, and although there have been many brave and admirable attempts to develop and perfect the idea on a small scale, it can never work entirely. The poet John Donne knew why:

> No man is an island, entire of itself;
> every man is a piece of the continent, a part of the main.

Perhaps he was pre-empting Garrett Hardin's first law of ecology that I quoted earlier: 'Everything is connected to everything else.'

It is in any case impossible in practical terms for an individual or a small group to be entirely self-sufficient. In a utopian society, dense urban populations might evolve into loosely federated groups who were able to manage themselves on a semi-self-sufficient basis, but everyday life is essentially dependent on a wide-ranging interchange of materials, energy and skills, so self-sufficiency could never be absolute. There are no human closed systems.

The boundaries of all groups interconnect. If it is true in real life that the boundary of each person or family is continually penetrated by a number of needs, self-sufficiency is a myth. It becomes another way of saying 'I'm all right, Jack', and, like the rich man, putting up barbed wire to keep non-self-sufficient people out. For there is no such thing as self-sufficiency on the twentieth floor of a tower block and there can be no practicable plan for vegetable farming or using windmills on the roof of a Glasgow tenement. It is relatively easy to be self-sufficient on a Welsh hill or on any patch of arable land large enough for self-support, but the alternative lifestyle here is more properly called farming.

A clear gap between idealism and reality has thus developed, which has led to the collapse of many rural communes. This is in part traceable to the discovery by the communards that they have achieved an isolation which carries little evolutionary potential. Once a commune has achieved a self-sustaining vegetable garden and managed to acquire warmth and shelter, there seems often to be a short period of balance and happiness. But this is almost inevitably followed by a run-down and eventual break-up.

I do not at all want to minimize the splendid and courageous achievements of the many groups who have cut themselves free of the conditioning processes of technological society. I admire them. But I want to suggest that there is an alternative way of looking at life which *does* carry evolutionary potential, and which could provide a continuous stimulus for evolution which would keep small groups together with the common external purpose of living with Gaia.

I also recognize the truth that many of the solutions to rural-urban problems are political, and stem from one of the most basic issues of human politics: the ownership and management of the land.

It is also clear that we in the West have no right whatever to act as moral exemplars to any of the citizens of developing countries who have just managed to raise their lifestyles above the bare subsistence level. I obviously cannot offer moral caveats to people in this position. If I were even to begin to suggest to them that the fruits of technological civilization are polluting and dangerous and that they must therefore not use them, I would be laughed out of court. These issues too are political; functions of the inequitable sharing of available resources and I do not want to deal with them in this book. I believe that there are much more urgent priorities to be developed first, which stem entirely from eventualities *outside* the human condition.

Further, I suspect that the net increase in entropy in the communist countries is very similar to that in Japan, Europe and America, and I see no more serious attempt to live higher up the solar drive chain on that side of the political divide than I do in the West. Power-based nation-states are all still grimly in pursuit of the 'technological fix', and everywhere people of both communist and capitalist societies turn, they are confronted with the same technological 'success' story. Concrete motorways unroll and steel and glass monoliths jut skywards, replicating themselves like giant robots until all cities begin to look exactly alike. The course of individual life is inexorably linked to money, employment, house, mortgage, car, annual holiday and a decent burial; 1984 in fact occurred about the real year 1960, when the development of data control and computing systems rendered privacy and human difference officially extinct, and when the media arrived at a consensus about visual symbols of normality.

As individuals, we clearly cannot alter such large-scale systems. But as individuals we can refute and reject as much of the industrial society as possible. We can decide which parts of the toymakers' official paradise we can do without. And so in the end we can change institutions by refusing their products.

Now this is clearly a statement of *revolution*, and I want to define exactly what I mean by the use of this dangerous word.

I mean simply a transformation – not a revolution by violence or by dictatorial action from left or right. I am not interested in another exhortation to barricades and death, nor in the creation of another authoritarian system which again restricts human freedom and continues the destruction of the earth organism. What I am talking about is a transformation to evolve a new philosophy, based on the premise that *no* action can be performed which does harm to Gaia. This philosophy will accept that the bodies of men and women of all races, rich and poor, powerful and weak, policemen and prisoners, are all equally susceptible to the man-made poisons which now circulate the planet; that there is no place for anyone to hide and no war to be fought which can in any way rectify the situation and that no individual, however rich or powerful, can escape the entropy crisis.

The sections that follow therefore are intended as the basis for individual changes which can lead to such personal transformation. It is only by personal transformations of this kind that I believe the new philosophy can grow, and so lead to more general changes in society.

8

Eating the Sun

If it is true that we are what we eat, then plant-eating animals are composed of the sun, and the bodies of technical men are made of coal, gas and oil.

The habits of the plant eaters are as high up the solar drive chain as it is possible to be, and they produce the minimum change in entropy. The eating habits of Western man are low down the solar drive chain and produce a very large increase in entropy. I am not going to suggest, therefore, that people start to wander the field grazing. But I do suggest we make a reappraisal of how we eat.

The principles of the solar drive chain lead naturally to the idea of the *food chain*. In the absence of man, food chains are integrally related to the solar drive, but in the presence of man this relationship has been destroyed.

A food chain is a sequence of events between the incoming energy of the sun and the consumption of food (Fig. 3).

The rays of the sun are collected by plants, the plants are eaten by animals, then the plant-eating animals are eaten by flesh-eating animals and finally the flesh-eating animals are consumed by man. In a closed ecosystem, this situation is normally restored by the decay process in the ground which first breaks down the waste products of the food chain by bacterial and fungal action and then re-creates nutrients for the plants in a continuous and viable cycle with a very low total entropy release.

But the energy wastage even in this sequence is immense. At each step, on average about 90 per cent of the energy in the previous step is lost without issue, either in inefficient chemical transfer or in waste heat released to the environment. For example, one study using body weight as a standard shows that for a person to gain one pound in weight from a fish diet, it is necessary to eat ten pounds of fish. The fish ate 100 pounds of shrimp and worms and the shrimp and worms consumed nearly 1,000 pounds of plankton from the water; 1,000 pounds of plankton for one pound of man! Someone who is two stone overweight, therefore, has diverted nearly five tons of plankton to make surplus fat. This ratio of ten to one keeps on recurring in studies of food efficiency, and provided that it is seen only as an approximation, it does offer a simple insight into the need to eat higher up the solar drive chain, and leads naturally to the argument for what I have called *low entropy eating*.

Incoming solar energy can drive 1,000 calories into one pound of rice. And one person can draw ten calories from one pound of rice. Conversely every 1,000 calories of solar energy drives 1,000 calories into grass. Cattle draw ten calories from eating the grass, and man draws one calorie from eating the cattle.

Another way of looking at the problem is to see how many people can be supported at each stage of the food chain. One study[1] shows that one person can live for one year on 600 trout, which live on 180,000 frogs, which live on 54,000,000 grasshoppers, which consume 2,000 tons of grass. But take one step along this food chain – eat the frogs rather than the trout, that is – and 30 people can live on 180,000 frogs which eat 54,000,000 grasshoppers which consume 2,000 tons of grass.

A diet of frogs, grasshoppers and grass is not exactly cordon bleu cuisine. But it does illustrate the main point about low entropy eating: that the number of people who can survive off a particular ecosystem increases as food consumption rises up the food chain towards the sun.

So the first rule of low entropy eating is: *To eat food which is created as high up the food chain as is possible.*

The consequences of this simple statement are immense. Let us look first at what a good diet needs:

1. Protein.
2. Carbohydrate.
3. Fat.

[1] Peterson, Z. P. G. Reporter quoted in: *Energy and Environment*. G. Tyler Millar Jn. Wadsworth Publishing Co. Inc., Belmont, California.

4. Vitamins.
5. Minerals.

And now let us look at what a real-life diet in a high technology society consists of:

1. Processed protein.
2. Processed carbohydrate.
3. Processed fat.
4. Processed vitamins.
5. Processed minerals.
6. Processed food additives.
7. Food colourings.
8. Man-made chemicals.

In addition, such a diet uses:

1. Deep freezers, tins, plastic containers, juggernauts, glass and metals.
2. Fossil fuels.

Our pattern of eating creates a massive increase in entropy in the form of process-waste heat, pollution and waste materials. In addition, the part of the food chain cycle which could have re-created plant nutrients out of animal and human waste is destroyed, since garbage is collected, burnt or dumped where it can never again make a useful contribution to entropic balance by ordinary organic decay in the ground. The cycle of viability is broken.

How our eating pattern has gone wrong can be broken down into three areas: (1) Where the food is grown; (2) How the food is processed; and (3) What food is eaten.

Let us look first at where the food is grown. Recalling that this book is for the individual, one individual clearly cannot alter farming methods or policy. But it is still worthwhile taking a brief look at two methods of farming, since an individual can choose, at least to some extent, where his food comes from.

The first need however is to eat less. If we refer back to the tenfold relationship, we can see that every calorie of food not eaten represents at least a thousand calories of waste heat and entropy saved.

Eat a sausage and you have one sixth of a cup of petrol. Eat an apple or a nut and there are only sunbeams in your stomach.

Books and articles on calorie requirements are legion, and there are a hundred and one different ways of losing weight. Except for rare medical conditions, fatness is due to eating too much, and being overweight is a real contribution to the planetary heat sink and to disorder.

Now let us look at where the food we do eat comes from. Non-industrial agriculture produces food with a very small increase in entropy. Figure 7, for example, shows the general layout of events on a farm using only animal and human power, operating a crop rotation, and bringing no artificial fertilizers in through the boundary. So, with human and animal muscle power combined with nutrient fertilizers supplied by the decay cycle inside the farm boundary, the rise in entropy is at a minimum and the product emerges through the boundary.

An industrial farm, Figure 8, is different. Animal and human muscle power is replaced by the tractor and the combine harvester. A sort of fertility is maintained by the import of artificial fertilizer and crops are kept free of disease by the use of sprays and pesticides. Tractors consume oil; artificial fertilizers are made from oil by an entropy intensive process; and pesticides are complex molecules fashioned from oil or coal bases. So the resultant rise of disorder or entropy on an industrial farm is large; there is a heavy contribution of pollution from the oil refineries and the fertilizer plants outside the farm boundary, as well as from the machinery inside the farm boundary. As one writer has commented: a potato is no longer made from the energy of the sun but from petrol.[2]

But no one is going to persuade the average farmer voluntarily to leave his tractor cab and return to a freezing wet trudge behind a horse-drawn plough. And no one can doubt that industrialization has increased agricultural output; it was possible to gather only 15 hundredweights of wheat from an acre in 1930, whereas in 1970 the yield was up to 34 hundredweights per acre.[3] But at the same time the total energy input to

[2] Odum, H. T. *Environment, Power and Society.* J. Willy, New York, 1971
[3] *UK Wheat Yield.* HMSO, 1966.

Natural Farm

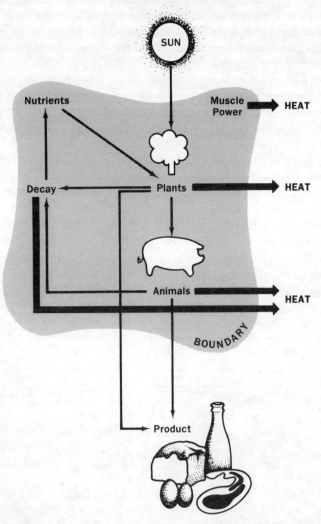

Figure 7

agriculture has risen from a figure of about 25 units[4] in 1930 (though the figure may well be far lower), to over 110 units in 1970. So the trade-off is increased yield against the increased energy to work an industrialized system. This would seem to be fair enough; except for the greatly increased entropy and pollution which results from the industrial system and which does not appear in the calculations.

If an individual cannot change farming methods or policy, what is the low entropy eater to do? He or she can refuse to eat the products of the industrialized food industry. This means discovering the origins of our food, buying only from suppliers of 'organically' grown food.

Industrial farming is bad enough, but the effects of food processing and technology are more dangerous still, not only to the fabric of the earth organism but also to our health and survival.

It is now quite clear that large sections of the food industry are systematically poisoning the public. Food which starts off as a perfectly natural mixture of nutrients is subjected to a series of technical procedures which would make an alchemist blanch. Man-made materials of no nutrient value are added, valuable foods are extracted, and texture, colour and taste are all changed by additives to meet images of perfection deliberately designed to deceive. But first of all, what is a food additive?

It is any substance added to a food which was not originally present, so a food colouring is an additive and so is a vitamin. A food flavouring is an additive and so is a protein. So, additives can be nutritionally useful or useless.

Additives have to be tested by experiment, mainly on animals, to satisfy the law. They are usually looked at for acute toxicity and long-term hazard such as carcinogenicity or teratogenicity (cancer production or leading to abnormal birth).

Testing for poisonousness usually relies upon an antiquated method called the LD/50 test, wherein an increasing dose of the additive is given to a series of animals until 50 per cent are killed. This is a crude and unreliable technique from which few

---

[4] 1 Unit=10^9 kilowatt hours energy equivalent.

Industrial Farm

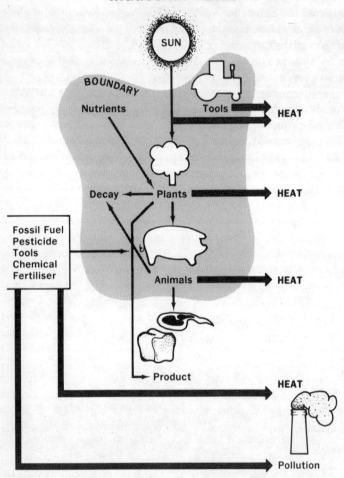

Figure 8

useful observations can be made, quite apart from the destruction of the large number of animals, after periods of prolonged and often appalling suffering.

Potential carcinogenicity is usually tested by giving regular doses of the substance under test to animals for their whole lifetime, and then examining the gut lining and other tissues for signs of malignant change. Sometimes the substance is applied to the skin or mucous membrane to see whether it will cause a surface cancer.

Teratogenicity is looked for by breeding animals after they have been given the substance for long periods, to see whether their offspring develop any physical or behavioural abnormality. This property was looked for in the case of Thalidomide.

All three principal methods are now coming under increasing scrutiny since there is growing disbelief in the validity of comparing animal and human reactions to poisons. This doubt has already been cynically exploited by some particularly mendacious manufacturers, who manage to pervert logic to the extent that they argue both that 'we have tested the substance on animals and find no toxic reactions at all, therefore the substance is safe for humans to eat'; and that 'we agree that some animals have shown adverse reactions, but of course it is quite impossible to compare animal to human reactions, therefore we think that there is no hazard and it is safe to eat'. This Catch 22 argument proves only that animals are being killed for purely legal reasons and no credible evaluation of hazard is being obtained. Heads the manufacturers win and tails the consuming public, and the animals, lose.

In some quite rare instances there may be nutritional advantage in adding vitamins, protein, carbohydrate or fat to prime foodstuffs. But there is no conceivable justification for adding colours, flavours, thickening agents, foaming agents, stabilizers or anti-oxidants, all of which are purely chemically derived and none of which has ever truly been shown to be free of hazard. They are useful only to the cynical opportunism of the food salesmen.

A good generalization about food additive toxicity is that the more complex a man-made molecule is, the more likely it is to be hazardous to man. A recent study by an American medical association concluded that up to 70 per cent of all human cancer may be due to man-made chemicals, and led one scientist to remark that: 'To live safely it will be necessary to live as far away from man-manipulated molecules as possible.'

There is no equivalent in British legislation of the American 'Delaney Clause'. The clause is an amendment to the 1958 US Food, Drug and Cosmetic Act and states that 'any substance which causes cancer when fed at any level to man or animal is specifically prohibited'.

Many dyes are used in this country which have been banned by the Food and Drug Administration in the United States: a sure indication of scientific incompetence. For example. 'Green 1' was banned in America in 1966 because it caused liver cancer in animals. 'Red 4' was banned in 1960 for producing damage to the adrenal gland and 'Yellows 1 & 2' were stopped in 1960 because they produced intestinal lesions at high dose-rates.

These food cosmetics are usually made of complex molecules derived from coal-tar oil derivatives. Their price is rising sharply because of their origin, and their sole purpose is to fool the consumer into gustatory ecstasy at the expense of his health. The food looks nice, but ruins the body.

The total number of food additives used at any one time may be as high as 20,000, and during the course of one year an average consumer may swallow three pounds of chemical substances which are not normally constituents of food.[5] Even if, impossibly, each one had been properly tested for safety, the tests themselves are at best a quasi-legal protection for the manufacturers should one of their products kill someone.

To eat 'natural' food has long been labelled as the province of faddists and cranks. Certainly there is a growing 'Health Food' industry which makes exaggerated claims for expensive extracts of nutritionally useless plants. It is not my intention to get involved in this particular debate. But when opponents of natural food enthusiasts state, with some relish, that 'all food is chemicals', they ignore a central fact: that additives are man-made chemicals whereas the chemicals of ordinary food are sun-made. It is not only the poisonous nature of technologically

---

[5] Editorial: *Lancet* 16 August 1969.

processed foods at issue here, but also the considerable misuse of fossil fuel and the very large contribution to the planetary load of disorder and pollution.

Two books go into the details of some of the poisons we eat and will help low entropy eaters to plan a less lethal and more Gaian diet. These are: (1) *Your Daily Food*, Doris Grant, Faber and Faber, London 1973; (2) *Food for a Future*, J. W. Tyson, Abacus Books, London 1976.

But now, to illustrate the effect on the earth organism of eating processed food, I am going to analyse two of our staple foods in more detail: bread and meat.

9

Half a Loaf

Whiteness is a powerful conditioning factor. We are encouraged by the advertising industry to add 'new whiteness' to clothes, to leave our sinks and lavatories shining white and to paint our homes with a pigment so super white that it dazzles the eye. Whiteness has become synonymous with purity, cleanliness and social success and is a potent symbol of achievement. Heroines dress in white and villains in black.

And so white flour sells not to feed us, but to purify our image. And this is not a recent deceit. The aristocrats of ancient Greece and Rome thought that it was preferable to eat white bread for similar reasons, and succeeding cultures have nearly always related it closely to wealth and prestige. But if all the evidence is assessed, it is now quite clear that white flour is damaging to health, nutritionally less effective than brown, and entropically unacceptable. What are the facts?[1]

The single wheat grain is made of three parts: the *endosperm* or white centre, the *germ* which is the growth centre and the *bran* or hard outer covering. The grain is a tiny masterpiece of design, a little package of growth and survival information. Each part contains valuable nutrients. The bran provides vitamins and minerals, the endosperm contains protein and carbohydrates and the germ is a mixture of vitamins, oils and minerals. When the grain is ground into ordinary flour, it is an almost perfectly balanced mixture of food.

Whole grain bread also makes a positive contribution to health. Good medical evidence is now available to relate lack of

[1] Easily the best informed and most formidable attack on the white loaf is *Bread* by Dr Ira Kaufman and others. A TACC report by Intermediate Publishing, Kettering, Great Britain, 1974. Much of the data supporting this section is taken from this excellent work.

fibre in food to a number of diseases. For example, cancerous changes in the large bowel,[2] coronary heart diseases,[3] and colonic diverticulae or pouch formation in the gut wall[4] have all been related to the absence of fibre (bran) in the diet.

Not so long ago a baker ground wheat, added salt, water and yeast, made the dough, let it rise and cooked a loaf. Nothing was added or subtracted from the flour and no additives were used.

But modern white bread is a high technology industrialized food, which bears little if any resemblance to its original constituents.

At the time of writing, a 'standard' sliced loaf costs 38 pence and its appearance makes it difficult to decide whether to eat it or to use it to tile the ceiling.

But more relevant to my theme is the enormous cloud of entropy produced by the complex machinery of the bread factory, the juggernaut which transports the product and the packaging process. Not only have we become conditioned to eating a fraudulent, sticky mixture of man-made chemicals which is sold on the crunch in its packaging; we have enormously increased the subsequent disorder.

I have found that I can grind one pound of flour with a hand grinder in four minutes, and make the equivalent weight of a standard loaf of bread for 9 pence, including the cost of the gas for cooking. The initial outlay for the grinder was £8.50. But this is a cash image of improvement and it takes second place to the decrease in entropy. My own small-scale hand process produces waste heat from the muscles of the body, and some pollution from the flue of the cooker.

Let us now examine in detail the entropy production of industrial bread. The industrial bread process starts off with the wheat grain, which is ground, not between stones as it once was, but in high-speed roller mills usually made of stainless steel. Stainless steel is a mixture of ordinary steel and a relatively rare metal, chromium, so right at the beginning we have to take into account the mining, smelting, refining and fabrication process of stainless steel with its large-scale entropy. Then the flour is

[2] Burkitt, D. P. 1971 *Cancer* 28 (1) 3.

[3] Trowell, H. C. 1972 *Rev. Eunop d'Etudes Clin et biol.* 17 (4) 345.

[4] Painter, N. G. Burkitt, D. P. 1971 *Brit. Med.* 3 (ii) 450.

extracted, which simply means that parts of the whole wheat are removed. Then by a process of ineluctably insane logic, it is reasoned that because some ingredients of the flour have been removed they must be replaced – not by the same products, but substitutes which are alleged to have similar properties.

To make white flour, two ingredients are removed, the bran and the wheat germ. This is done by 'bolting', where the whole flour falls through a series of grilles or cloths of different mesh sizes so that the larger particles of bran and germ are held back and the smaller, white particles of the endosperm fall through. Degrees of extraction are given as percentages. That is to say, wholewheat flour is spoken of as 100 per cent extraction and white flour as 70 per cent extraction, or 30 per cent missing. Grades of brownness or wholeness lie between the two figures.

Already, twenty-four vitamins and minerals have been reduced in the process by an amount varying between 40 per cent and 96 per cent.[5] So now comes the process optimistically entitled 'enrichment'. Twenty-four ingredients important to health having been removed, four are then replaced, and it is asserted that the flour has now been restored to nutritional equivalence with the original – a statement showing more confidence than accuracy. Vitamin B1 (thiamine), niacin, iron and chalk are added to replace, for example, the original thiamine, riboflavin, niacin, vitamin B6, panthothenic acid, alpha-tocopherol, calcium, phosphorus, magnesium, potassium, sodium, chromium, manganese, iron, cobalt, copper, zinc, selenium and molybdenum. This is an odd conception of 'enrichment', especially when about half the thiamine appears to be destroyed by baking and the iron is in a chemical form which is poorly absorbed by the body.[6]

Now we have three more industrial processes to add to the high-speed grinding and bolting, each with its own cloud of entropy: the iron making, the vitamin making and the chalk making.

By now, the flour is nearly ruined, but not quite. The toymakers are endlessly ingenious.

[5] Schroeder, H. 1971. *Amer. J. Clin. Nutrition* 24, 467–9.
[6] Elwood, P. C. 1963. *Brit. Med. J.* January.

To attempt some cosmetic restoration of a now totally etio-lated product, other materials can be added. A choice of 1 bleaching agent, 9 improving agents, 4 preservatives, 4 emul-sifiers, 5 anti-oxidants and 1 colouring agent are available and permitted additives, which can find their way into the stomach of the consumer. Again it is not my point to emphasize the health dangers of this grisly array of image improvers, but to emphasize that each is the end product of an energy consumptive and entropy generating and polluting industry.

The considerable health hazards of these complex chemicals have been excellently debated in two recent books,[7,8], and both drew critical official comment. But one governmental committee considering preservatives in general commented on flour addi-tives that 'in no case do we regard the data as adequate for the expression of a final opinion'.[9] The point is that it is simply not possible to test any food additive adequately. And the twenty-four permitted chemicals I listed have only one function: to delude the public into finding the standard white loaf is attrac-tive to look at, to feel and to chew. It is surely a criminal act of opportunistic commercialism to create a product which is attrac-tive to the senses but poisonous to the body.

In the white loaf you may consume Polyoxyethylene mono-stearate, which allows flour to absorb more water. You may eat Potassium bromate, which allows the wet flour to hold more air. You could swallow Ammonium chloride, which assists fermen-tation. And you could be digesting Propionic acid which retards mould formation.

Polyoxyethylene, Potassium bromate, Ammonium chloride and Propionic acid are all complex man-made molecules and each is a product of a separate entropic polluting industrial process.

Finally, the industrial loaf has to be wrapped, transported and marketed, and each of these processes can be looked at in terms of relative fuel costs.[10]

[7] *Bread*. TACC report 1974, op cit.

[8] *Your Daily Food*. Doris Grant. Faber & Faber, 1973.

[9] Food Standards Committee, Appendix V. Report on Flour Improvers, HMSO, 1960.

[10] *Fuel's Paradise*. Dr P. Chapman. Penguin Books, 1975.

Function	Per cent Fuel	Place
Shop heat and light	8.6	Retail
Transport	12.6	Bakery
Other Ingredients	9.4	
Baking Fuel	8.3	Bakery
Transport	5.0	
Packaging	2.2	
Other	2.0	Mill
Milling Fuel	7.4	
Transport	1.4	
Other		
Tractor Fuel	7.3	Farm
Fertilizer	11.6	

I have treated bread in detail, not only because it is a prime food, but also because it is a practical example of how a habit can be changed which not only improves health, saves money and avoids the consumption of poisons, but also makes a direct and real contribution to the reduction of personal entropy debt.

People often object to the idea of home baking on the grounds that they do not have enough time. But against this, the cost reduction from 38 to 9 pence is significant over, say, a year (a family using 1 large loaf a day would save £51). And as prices rise there may well come a time when people will begin to allocate their working time differently; and choose not to put all of it into work outside the boundary of their home to earn money to buy food. They may divide work into labour to make money outside the boundary, and labour to save money inside the boundary. I shall develop this point in a later section.

How do you cost your own labour? The answer is you don't. The four minutes of muscle work necessary to make one pound of flour is ordinary good exercise and saves having to buy chest-expanders to keep fit. An Indian Swami recently told me that he meditates while grinding flour. That seems a good idea too. So much for bread, now for meat.

10

Meat and Disorder

About 90 per cent of the available agricultural land in the United Kingdom is used for the support of livestock raised upon protein foods which could be directly eaten by people.

In the developed countries, as much high-protein cereal is used for animal feed as is used in developing countries as food for the people themselves. The United States, for example, imported 700,000 tons of fishmeal from Chile and Peru in 1968 for use as animal feed; this contained enough protein to supply the entire population of Peru.

Cattle are highly inefficient protein makers. The weight of protein they have to consume to produce one pound of meat is called the *protein conversion ratio*. At one time, cattle grazed on grass, but now in the technological flesh industry they must consume 21.4 lb of prime vegetable or fish protein to make one pound of beef on the animal: a total loss of protein in a society which puts protein into shampoo for no other reason than to glue the ends of split hairs together.

Another way of looking at the conversion efficiencies of plants and animals is to measure the amount of protein each one makes from one acre of land. Cereals produce five times as much protein as meat, peas and beans ten times more and spinach twenty-six times more.[1]

Another estimate shows that soya beans can produce 260 kg of protein per acre, lucerne 675 kg per acre and prime grade beef a mere 49kg.[2]

Prime grade beef is also different from the ordinary grades in one other respect. It contains 63 per cent more *fat* than the

[1] Wokes, F. *Plant Foods for Human Nutrition* 1 (No. 1) 32, 1968.
[2] Bray, W. J. *New Scientist*, April 1976. Data adapted from *Journal of Agric. & Food Chem.* 13, 145, 1965.

standard grades. The fat is in the form of 'marbled' fat which surrounds each muscle fibre, and it is put there by a three-month process of special overfeeding which is described by the trade with a gallows humour as *finishing*.

In the cycling and recycling within the undisturbed earth organism, both animal and human wastes are returned to plants as nutrients by the process of decay (Figs 3 and 5). But in the technological flesh industry, so much excreta is produced by the aggregation of animals in dense 'factory' conditions that it becomes impossible to return all their waste to the land locally, and it is either transported elsewhere with a further use of energy, dumped into waterways as a pollutant, or burnt, so that all its potential turns into entropy.

In the world at large, about 40 per cent of all livestock is derived from vegetable protein directly suitable for human consumption. To reduce the population of livestock by 50 per cent would release about 100 million tons of grain for human consumption.[3] These figures show that to eat meat is to employ two separate areas of the planet's surface, and the solar energy falling on them, in order to eat something which contains no increase in protein concentration over that of the animal feed. Thus to eat meat is to eat very low down the solar drive chain and to squander entropy. In fact, one acre of soya bean makes five times as much protein as beef can make from the same area, and so to eat meat rather than soya beans is actually to use up two areas of the earth's surface to produce a net protein loss.

What does meat eating do to people? Earlier I described the *food chain*. Man feeds on fish which feed on shrimps which feed on plankton. Each species is linked to its neighbour by a chain of consumption. But as animals feed on each other, some have the ability to concentrate materials from the bodies of their prey.

Although many food authorities keep the addition of pesticides to animal feed as low as possible for this reason, as pesticides move up the food chain, their relative concentration in flesh may also rise. One American study, for example, shows that where root vegetables contain only 0.007 parts per million of pesticide

[3] Kottman, R. M. Pearlberg, D. *Proc. Nat. Inst. Animal Agric.* 16, 1966.

residue (Organochlorine), leaf vegetables contain 0.036 ppm and meat 0.281 ppm: meat therefore showing an almost 300 per cent increase in pesticide content over root vegetables. No one seems clear how the animals managed to ingest the pesticides, particularly since their primary foodstuffs were relatively free. The concentration seems to arise from a number of indirect sources in the environment.

Some years ago, it was discovered that the addition of certain sex hormones increased the macabre 'flesh per carcase yield' in the abattoir. And then it was found that some of the hormones (notably di-ethyl-stilboestrol) were stored in the animal and therefore consumed by the customer. There was an outcry, an investigation and a far from general ban on the use of these substances. They are banned in the USA but it is still possible for them to be used in Britain. Indeed the Voluntary Veterinarian Products Safety Protection scheme has averred that it is safe to use them,[4] in spite of a body of evidence which strongly suggests that di-ethyl-stilboestrol is capable of producing cancer in man. Similarly, antibiotics are still added to feedstuffs in spite of the recommendations against such a practice of the Swann Committee Report.[5]

Indiscriminate ingestion of antibiotics can also lead to the emergence of the transferable drug resistance I have already described where an antibiotic resistant factor in the bacteria exposed to antibiotics can be transferred not only to other disease-causing bacteria, but also to other non-disease-causing bacteria so that the resistance factor can be transferred. When the bacteria – newly trained in resistance – are transferred to someone else, they may cause fresh disease which is resistant to antibiotics.

To summarize, we find ourselves in a real-life situation which it would be impossible to write credibly about as science fiction. Ninety per cent of agricultural land in the UK is used for the production of livestock which is fed with human-compatible protein at a total loss ratio of over twenty to one. Some of the animals are then specially fed to increase the fat content of the meat, and kept under conditions which make the reuse of their

[4] *Your Daily Food.* Doris Grant. Faber & Faber, London 1973.
[5] *Report of the Joint Committee on the Use of Antibiotics in Animal Husbandry & Veterinary Medicine.* HMSO. Pigfood may still contain stilboestrol (May 1977).

manure impossible. Matters are then arranged so that the meat may contain high concentrations of pesticide, sex-hormones and antibiotics all of which are injurious to health. And then to cap it all, some of it may be tinned and thus absorb the dangerous heavy metal lead, up to levels which are officially recognized as dangerous to health. (Although an official 'safe dose' of lead of five parts per million is sanctioned except in the case of baby foods, much higher amounts have been recorded in both meat and fish.)[6]

But the 'beef steak economy' persists. An Indian, on average, may consume only 2.85 lb of meat in one year. An American may consume on average 212 lb of meat – which is 12 per cent more than his body can use and 45 per cent more than his total body protein need.

This evidence alone would be more than sufficient to make the consumption of meat impossible on a rational basis, but there are other factors which are more directly relevant to my thesis.

The body of Gaia, the earth spirit, is made up of every living creature within its whole, and by the process of evolution, each species has attained its own existence within the balanced whole. Although millions of different life-forms may disappear totally as a result of circumstance, competition and disaster, those that remain represent the result of a total planetary experience of balanced, stable co-existence. Clearly the species prey on each other. Gazelles eat plants, and lions eat gazelles, but with one great difference from our own situation: they do so of necessity. They have no choice.

The lion *is* carnivorous and there is nothing the lion can do about it. But we have the language, the data, the reasoning capacity, the imagination and the freedom to choose and to act. We also have enough data to show that plants easily provide us with a diet which is equivalent in nutritional terms to the consumption of meat.

Freedom implies a *choice* which affects *action*. And freedom of action implies a sense of *responsibility*. Our responsibility must be first to Gaia and second to ourselves.

[6] *Survey of Lead in Food.* Ministry of Agriculture & Fisheries 1972. HMSO.

No single human being can avoid the killing of individual members of the Gaian life-form. Each time even a vegan breathes in, an uncountable number of bacteria perish in the moisture of his or her lungs. Each time water is boiled, micro-species perish, and each time a lettuce is eaten, its life process ceases. Each species on the planet is part of an inevitable consumer chain and either eats or dies.

Nature is neither kind nor cruel, beautiful nor ugly: it is just nature. But *we* as a *species* have *feelings* of compassion about it. Few believe a rose to be ugly and few believe the interior of a supermarket to be beautiful.

It is difficult to feel compassion for inhaled bacteria or a lettuce, but it is impossible not to feel compassion for a young calf surrounded by a mist of fear and terror as it is pulled struggling into the white-tiled slaughter room on its way to becoming *escalope de veau*.

Why do we feel this? Not just because the calf is beautiful; not just because the calf is young and innocent; and not just because it is suffering. But because we have been the sole cause of pain, terror and suffering to an innocent and beautiful creature for *totally unnecessary reasons*.

If there were nothing else to eat and I possessed a gun I would shoot animals for food. But the calf is part of the earth organism and where there is no survival need to eat meat, it has a *right* to live on a part of the earth and a *right* not to be taken for food by an already overfed species. The rights of an animal arise from existence and tenancy of the planet in the same way that ours do. We exert those rights, the animals cannot, because they are powerless.

No single species has an automatic right to dominate the living and non-living fabric of the planet. But we have assumed that right, and this has distorted our aesthetic enjoyment of the life around us. It is entirely hypocritical to take our children to the countryside to look at the 'pretty lambs' if we know that on the same evening we are going to eat one roasted with rosemary and garlic. Consciousness of this unnecessary exploitation makes our enjoyment an intellectual rather than a feeling experience.

If I know some part of nature is beautiful to me, it is irrational to damage or destroy it unless I have to. It will no longer be beautiful, and I shall end up with blunted sensitivities.

At the time of writing I am a vegetarian of a mere two and a half years' standing. I feel entirely different: fitter, calmer and more easy in the body. Whether this is due to mind, heart or stomach I do not know, but the lambs *are* beautiful. Also I find myself joining an interesting band of people: Charles Darwin, Ralph Waldo Emerson, Benjamin Franklin, John Milton, Isaac Newton, Bernard Shaw, Alexander Pope, Rousseau, Shake-speare, Tagore, Leonardo da Vinci, Wagner, Tolstoy and Plutarch.

It was Tolstoy who wrote that 'a vegetarian diet is the acid test of humanitarianism', and Plutarch who stated that 'Man makes use of flesh not out of want and necessity, seeing that he has the liberty to make his choice of herbs and fruit, the plenty of which is inexhaustible; but out of *luxury* and being cloyed with necessities, he seeks after impure and inconvenient diet, pur-chased by the slaughter of living beasts; by showing himself more cruel than the most savage of wild beasts.'

Not all Christians are vegetarian, yet Jesus as quoted in the original Essene version of the Gospel says:

And the flesh of slain beasts in his body will become his own tomb. For I tell you truly, he who kills himself, and who so eats the flesh of slain beasts eats the body of death.

These quotations are taken from a recent book which puts the ethics and philosophy of vegetarianism in a passionate and magnificently researched manner.[7]

By rejecting meat, we can approach the beginnings of a Gaian ethic. We can re-create species interrelationship and eat higher up the solar drive chain, and so substantially reduce our contributions of entropy and pollution to the planetary substance.

The exploration of the vegetable world is an exciting voyage of discovery and for those who would like to experiment with high-protein meatless food, one book stands out again because it

[7] *Food for a Future*. Jon Wynne-Tyson. Abacus Books, London 1976.

is so carefully researched. In it, vegetable foods are compared on a weight basis against beef-steak equivalents of protein; and a scheme is set out showing which proteins are usable by the body. This is *Diet for a Small Planet*, by Frances Moore Lappé.[8]

[8] *Diet for a Small Planet*. Frances Moore Lappé. Friends of the Earth/ Ballantyne, New York 1971.

11

Packets of Disorder

The supermarket shelves are a garish riot of paper, plastic, metal and glass, skilfully designed to delude the buyer into believing that the contents of the package are as attractive as the picture on the wrapping. Metal forming, plastic moulding, screen printing, soldering, dyeing and psychological skills are all used in a concerted attempt to deceive the senses.

On the outside of a can of pears, for example, there is a delicately painted image of a luscious perfect fruit with yeast bloom frosting its skin. But inside there is a gritty, pallid machine-shaped lump of fruit-based material, soaked in syrup and flavouring, to which artificial lubricants may have been added so that the pieces of fruit slip seductively out of the tin.

So a first step towards change might be to recondition our perceptions and memory completely, to deny that the pieces in the tin bear any resemblance to a genuine pear, and conclude instead that they are an *industrial replica* which used the actual fruit from a tree only as a structural basis for a complex exercise in artefact construction and brainwashing. The solid pear shape could just as well have been cast in moulds from 'general pear purée' and then flavoured with 'pear flavouring', in much the same way as the sorry carcases of broiler chickens are injected with 'chicken flavour' to make them taste like chicken.

From there, it is a simple step to your next rule: completely avoid foods that have been subject to process and technology.

Now consider a tin. First, iron ore was dug out of the ground and smelted into iron in a blast furnace, voiding heat and polluting fumes into the air. The iron was turned into mild steel by a high-temperature oxygen process releasing more heat and pollution, and then the steel was forced through a rolling mill where it was squeezed into thin steel sheet.

The sheet was packaged and transferred to a large low-loading lorry which rumbled along a motorway, pouring fumes and noise, until it reached the tin-plating plant. Here the rare and expensive metal tin was applied to the steel, using large quantities of electricity and yet more heat. The tin-plated steel was then sent by another lorry, producing more noise and pollution, to the tin-making plant where it was cut, roll formed, soldered and lacquered, ending up as a tin ready for filling with pear replicas.

In another factory, an artist produced an original painting of a beautiful pear surrounded by graphics, trees were felled to make paper, colours were mixed so that a printed copy of the artist's work could be applied to the paper. The paper was gummed and the roll of pear image labels transferred by another lorry to the pear-canning factory.

The tins were filled with industrially shaped pear replicas, sealed, labelled, stored, distributed and sold.

Finally a consumer tore the can open with another brightly plated device called a can opener, and swallowed the pear replica. There was then a brief clatter as the whole exquisitely and skilfully produced tin hit the garbage can.

One hundred years later, the tin was a small and completely unusable patch of rust in the middle of a toxic morass of plastic and other materials in a garbage dump.

One soft drink currently on the market is encased in a deep-drawn one-piece aluminium can. Ninety-three per cent of the cost of this 'softest' of drinks is the cost of the aluminium can, and 7 per cent that of the contents: a poisonously undrinkable concoction of acids, colouring, flavouring and water.

Aluminium demands *seventeen times* the refining energy for its fabrication that steel does. And one of the biggest aggregations of empty soft-drink cans I have seen was on a rural commune, where everyone professed peace and love and where the 'alternative lifestyle' was all the rage.

So, as a third action, following the rejection of meat and

processed bread, we can resolve, as a direct way of reducing personal entropy debt, never to buy tinned food or drink again.

A tin is bad enough. But look next at a bottle of lemonade. Assume that the 'lemonade' – again made from a non-lemon-containing mixture of citric acid, saccharin, colouring, dissolved carbon dioxide and water – has been swallowed, and the bottle again ends up in the garbage can. What has been put there?

The glass container industry has a turnover of £175 million a year and accounts for one ninth of the entire packaging industry. In 1975 just over 3,000,000,000 separate glass containers were made.

Glass is made from 50 per cent silica sand, 20 per cent cullet (recycled glass), 16 per cent soda ash, 12 per cent limestone and 2 per cent of other materials such as pigmenting agents and fluxes. Sodium and calcium oxide may also be added to the mix as it enters the melting furnace.

The glass furnaces consume huge quantities of energy, which accounts for about 16 per cent of the final cost of the glass.

Approximately 60 per cent of this energy will find its way into the environment as waste heat, disorder and entropy. The glass container industry in Britain consumes about 10,730,000,000 kilowatt hours of energy annually.

Imagine ten thousand million one-bar electric fires left on for one hour, or one million for the entire year – quite apart from the despoliation of the landscape involved in the collection of the sand. And this to produce a throwaway container for the undrinkable.[1]

So, no more throwaway bottles. If a container does have to be taken home, make sure it is recycled or that it finds a second use.

We have been trained to buy food in containers delivered to us by the food manufacturers. Now we can reverse matters by taking a container to the shop or taking the food home without a container.

This is difficult and embarrassing. Taking articles without

[1] The figures in this section are taken from a recent and highly detailed survey of the glass container industry: *Many Happy Returns*, Richard Bate, Friends of the Earth, London 1976.

wrappings out of shops, I have to date been arrested three times by store detectives who have assumed that I have stolen the goods since they are unwrapped. All I can say here is: keep the cash slip. You get used to it, and so far as the detectives are concerned, they have all so far been studiously polite; which is a pity because I like a fight.

It also causes scenes at the bakers. Some devoted but irrational law-maker has decreed that bread must be wrapped. Actually the wrapping consists of a flimsy piece of tissue which fails to cover the whole surface of the loaf, so the whole thing is no more than a ritualized theatrical performance of the *idea* of cleanliness. But trees are cut down to make the paper.

You may of course argue that if the thing you have bought is already wrapped, there is no point in taking off the wrapping, since its entropic and pollution price has already been paid to the environment. The answer is that the action tells the shop-keeper how you feel. I bought a pair of socks in a London shop and handed the paper bag back to the shop assistant. He listened politely to my reasons for the action, but his face told me that he thought I was crazy. About a year later, I returned to the same shop for some T-shirts, the same assistant put the shirts in a bag, began to hand the bag to me, then glanced up at me, took it back, removed the bag and handed me the unwrapped T-shirts. His eyes still said 'you're crazy', but he smiled.

As far as possible, take permanent containers to the shop or take shopping home unpackaged.

It would be a very useful project for a design college to hold a competition for the best design of shopping basket with its own containers. There could be a butter compartment, a milk flask and various containers for loose materials like grain and sugar. All could be designed to fit together to avoid jostling and spillage.

Now things are getting more interesting. No meat, whole bread only, no tins, no bottles, no packaging at all and an avoidance of food which has been processed.

You will be thinking that I want us all to end up in the middle of a field wearing homespun loincloths and chewing dried beans. I do agree that what I have so far suggested limits choice, but I have found also that the limitations of choice constitute a stimulus and a liberation rather than a restriction, because they clear the vision and open the senses. Mine is not at all a recipe for a bleak and restrictive life, as I hope to show in part three: it is tremendous fun.

The point is that a series of rose-coloured filters have been lowered over our eyes so that we see the unspeakable as the consumable and the frankly poisonous as nutritious.

The actions I am suggesting are intended to have two results: first of all to clear the senses and remove the rose filters, and then to lead to a reduction in *personal entropy* debt.

I would like to look now at another delusion which is quite easy to eradicate: the idea that we can buy 'coffee' in the form of a tin of soluble granules.

12

A Cup of Dreams

Coffee is defined as: 'A watery infusion for drinking made from the roasted and ground seeds of the shrub Coffea.' The seeds are the coffee beans and all it takes is to grind them after they are roasted, and infuse them in boiling water.

Although it is apparently perfectly legal for a firm which fabricates 'instant coffee' to state on the label of the jar that the contents are 'made from one hundred per cent pure ground coffee' the process involved almost defies the imagination.

Coffee beans are delivered, roasted, ground and infused in large vats of very hot water. The resultant liquor is then fed to a series of huge stainless-steel devices called evaporators, which are heated by oil-fired steam until most of the water has been evaporated. Finally the now very sticky fluid is subjected to freeze drying, a process which involves large-scale refrigeration plants which reject huge volumes of heat to the air, and heavy electrically driven vacuum pumps which draw water vapour away from the frozen material. The solid cake is then crumbled, packed and sold as 'coffee'. It is not. It is a *coffee derivative*.

Although it is probably a literal truth that the final product is made from 'one hundred per cent ground coffee', since no other material has been added, the process involved uses large quantities of energy, is *totally unnecessary*, and makes a product which does not even begin to taste like an infusion made from the seeds of the shrub Coffea.

We consume a complex industrial artefact which bears no relationship at all to the original, and which has produced in its wake a great increase in the planetary loading of entropy, pollution and resource reduction.

After the cup of instant entropy, what about milk? Suppose

we add what is pedantically entitled 'non-dairy product substitute' instead. This is an easily soluble crumbly white powder and may contain: syrup, added dextrose, vegetable fat, sodium caseinate, dipotassium phosphate, emulsifier, sodium silico-aluminate, lecithin, unnamed flavourings, unnamed colourants. Each chemical had to be made by a separate industrial process. Each process had to be fuelled and driven, and each produced its inevitable entropy debt; all to produce a whitening and opacifying agent for a clear brown solution.

It is a standing joke among waiters on the restaurant car of a particular British Rail train to ask customers if they are enjoying the lovely smell of coffee. The customers enjoy the delicious aroma in the carriage until they are disillusioned by the waiter who points to the instant-coffee factory outside the window.

In summary, the aspiring Gaian will have no more convenient instant coffee, or convenient instant anything. 'Convenient' here is translatable as: energy consumptive, polluting and entropy generating. Is it really so much trouble to pour boiling water on to ground coffee and wait for five minutes?

A reminder here about my use of the word 'chemical'. As I have already said, it is a cliché used in their own defence by food technologists that all our food is made of chemicals. I am using the word to indicate man-made chemicals which unnecessarily offend the earth organism and may, in addition, be poisonous.

One more example of a high technology machine to which we have been mendaciously conditioned by the toymakers is the deep-freeze.

13

Frozen Seasons

A refrigerator for cooling food is one of the great boons produced by high technology. It uses a very small amount of energy, its basic operation, using the heat pump cycle, is the most efficient of engines, it lasts a very long time if properly maintained and it preserves a considerable quantity of food which would otherwise have gone bad. It is a real convenience.

A deep-freeze is entirely different. Although it works on the same principle as a refrigerator, it is sold principally on the assertion that food can be bought at its lowest price, then stored until it is eaten when the price may be higher. This is alleged to be economic. But at the time of writing, an average deep-freezer uses £32 worth of electricity over a year, and advertisements in second-hand magazines reveal that it can depreciate in value by three-fifths of its original price over the same period. Therefore a deep-freeze costing £150 may cost £128 in its first year of operation. However skilful the housewife becomes in buying cheaply, it is just not possible to save that amount of money, unless the freezer is emptied and refilled completely on a fortnightly basis and an average of 6 pence per pound of food stored is saved on purchase. All a deep-freeze provides is the opportunity to eat raspberries in January and sprouts in mid-summer; to freeze the seasons.

Now consider the whole process in terms of entropy debt. A complex industrial operation has to take place to prepare the food and to pass it through the deep-freeze process near its point of origin. The process of deep-freezing, again using the heat pump cycle, rejects or pumps away very large quantities of waste heat to the atmosphere to freeze the food. This entropy is irrecoverable since the heat is dispersed and cannot be recaptured. Now deep-frozen food is transferred by refrigerated juggernaut, which travels the highway trailing another cloud of rejected heat, noise and pollution behind it. The food is delivered to the frozen-food shop where it is stored in a battery of deep-freezers again using electrical energy at 28 per cent efficiency, and rejecting waste heat to the atmosphere. Finally the purchaser buys the icy lump and takes it home to store it in his own deep-freeze until he thaws it and eats it. It is in sum a complex industrial process which is specifically designed to reduce the flavour of the food and to lose the housewife money on the promise of raspberries in January.

So, out with the freezer.

Snags may yet turn up, but so far I have found living without these high technological accoutrements easy.

As a lifelong and devoted hedonist who loves food, I assumed when I started that the regime I had decided to adopt would make eating uninteresting. But instead, I have discovered an entirely new series of flavours and dishes. What is more, in spite of the derisive snort of a scientist to whom I showed an account of one week of my eating, who declared that if 'I went on like that I would get ill and get symptoms of malnutrition', I have been going on like that for over two years, I did not get ill and I do not have malnutrition. The scientist is still snorting.

Now a little about cooking.

14

Heating Machines for Food

A gas cooker I saw recently was priced at £950. It is equipped with a variety of switches, dials, time clocks and winking lights. It also has four gas rings, a grill, an oven and a spit-roaster. And it needs an electricity supply for its gas controls. About all it does not have is cognac on tap.

Another one cost £84. It also has four gas rings, a grill and an oven. It has no spit-roaster, there are no electronic controls and it does not therefore need an electricity supply.

The first cooker was advertised on the idea of 'quality'. Quality is an interesting concept and nowhere has it been more excitingly explored than in Robert Pirsig's splendid book *Zen and the Art of Motorcycle Maintenance* (1975). He talks of quality as a principle-force-elixir-godhead, way beyond the ordinary dualism of subjective and objective. But in the case of the expensive cooker, the word was used to imply that its design and construction are of better quality than that of cheaper cookers, and that to own it therefore would enrich living. In fact, the amount of heat emerging from its burners is the same as that produced by the burners of the £84 cooker, and both are built of heavy-weight stove-enamelled steel and stainless steel.

The luxury cooker does not cook food quicker or more elegantly, and it does not have a longer lifetime, given the same degree of care, as the cheaper one. The second cooker certainly lacks a spit-roast and electronic controls, so the owner cannot turn meat while it is cooking, nor can he or she go horse racing or play bingo while the cooker is lit, since it requires human attention. The difference between the two is nothing to do with quality.

The real difference (apart from £866 in cash) is one of shape and massiveness. In the expensive cooker every surface, door and handle has been exaggerated by a stylist, and uses *more* metal than the other. It has *more* stove enamel, *more* plating, *more* chrome-plated edging strips. It is also *more* difficult to use successfully – a training in computing logic would be an advantage. In a blind food-testing trial it would be impossible to distinguish which cooker had done the cooking. The more expensive cooker (costing nearly a quarter of the average national income per year) has trapped in its structure far more fabrication energy, and has therefore a higher contained entropy and pollution debt. The only additional function it subserves is to provide an image in hardware of financial success and prestige.

By paying more money, the richer purchaser thus incurs a far greater personal entropy debt. Conspicuous consumption, in other words, turns out to be anti-Gaian – a point which leads to the conclusion that to follow a Gaian ethic can form the logical basis of a more egalitarian society: *Gaianism* not socialism perhaps. This point I will return to.

Cooking can be done on a very significantly reduced amount of fuel, with far simpler heating machinery than we are used to. I have been experimenting with a saucepan insulated on its outer surface: so far, I have been able to cook over 2 pounds of vegetable stew with 3¼ inches of one-inch-diameter candle. I am not seriously suggesting that this is a sensible way to cook, but it illustrates just how much energy can be saved by alternative methods. It is even possible to cook without fuel.

15

Cool Cooking and Local Eating

The principle underlying the 'hay box' is centuries old. All you do is to heat food to boiling point and then surround the pot with as much insulation as possible, so that it cools as slowly as possible.

I did an experiment to show how this reduces the amount of fuel necessary for cooking by about two-thirds. I made an insulated container out of expanded polystyrene sheet rolled up into a cylinder with a lid. (Plastic you say! Yes, but the whole structure 22 inches high and 15 inches wide contained only 6 oz of plastic; and it could easily have been made out of wood and straw with only a small reduction in insulation efficiency.) I then filled a metal saucepan with two pints of water, put the lid on and brought it to the boil, put it on a table and measured the temperature of the water with a remote sensor every fifteen minutes until it fell to room temperature. I then boiled another two pints of water, in the same saucepan, but this time put the saucepan into the insulated container. Again I measured the temperature of the water every fifteen minutes. I found that the insulated pan took 5½ hours to fall to room temperature, while the uninsulated pan fell to the same temperature in 45 minutes. Since the process of cooking begins at about 60°C, the insulated pan would be continuing to cook its contents for 1¾ hours after it was taken off the cooker. Cooking took place during cooling *with no expenditure of fuel*.

In practice, it is only necessary to bring a heavy saucepan full of food to the boil, and keep it there for about two minutes to pump as much heat as possible into the system, then to put it into the insulated container. Even the most difficult of foods, such as beans, cook completely without further heating. And food cooked by cooling tastes absolutely delicious – I think the reason is that none of the flavours and smells is boiled off, it all remains in the food.

Eating locally produced food also has the inherent attractions that it is likely to be fresh and tasty; and that the consumer will find it easier to discover the origin of the food and get to know the producer. But it also carries with it another less obvious advantage: it reduces the personal entropy debt of the consumer.

One American study[1] showed that to assemble the components of a hamburger and milk-shake on a tray at a drive-in in New Jersey, a total of 7,141 lorry miles involving 30 separate lorry trips had to be made: 360 for the plastic spoon, 1,350 for the paper straws, 1,372 for the milk-shake, 250 for the pickles, 1,350 for the beef, 1,779 for the roll, 405 for the onion and 275 for the salt. Each lorry mile travelled entails diesel fuel burnt, release of waste heat and production of non-degradable garbage. So the closer the origin of the food to your mouth, the better it is for Gaia and the lower the personal entropy debt.

[1] Life Science Library, *Wheels*. W. Owen, E. Bowen. Time Life International, Nederland NV. 1963.

16
Water

We need water to drink, to irrigate crops, to wash bodies and to clean places. Where does fresh water come from? It arises from a rather ugly-sounding system called the *hydrologic cycle* which suggests that there is a logical machine somewhere in the sky making it all happen. I shall call it the *water cycle*.

We can start describing a cycle at any point. Let us begin with the sea. As the sun shines, water evaporates from the surface of the sea, and cools to form clouds. Some water also evaporates from the land and this adds to the clouds. Some clouds move inland on the wind and cool, so condensing their water as rain or snow. The rain soaks into the earth, some of it evaporates again, some reaches the rivers and some soaks down through the ground into underground water channels. The water in the rivers and the underground channels finds its way to the sea, completing the cycle. The whole process is driven by the sun and is really a planet-wide solar still, but only a self-regulating one as long as technical man has nothing to do with it.

The amount of fresh water available to us is astonishingly small. If all the world's water were lumped together and called 100 per cent, then 97 per cent of it would be sea-water and only 3 per cent fresh. But of that 3 per cent, over 2.9 per cent is frozen into the polar ice-caps, which means that only 0.1 per cent of the world's fresh water is available to the entire life process of the planet. One recent estimate suggests that Europeans extract three times the amount of water that they return to accessible reserves, and Americans two times. This means that the *water table* (that is the level of the water soaked into the land underfoot) is falling.

Plants use water copiously since water is in a continuous

process of transpiration: that is to say, it is continually rising up the stem of the plant and being lost through the leaves as water vapour. For example: to grow one corn plant takes about 50 gallons of water, to harvest one pound of wheat takes 60 gallons and one pound of rice a massive 230 gallons. But all these figures pale beside the 2,500 to 6,000 gallons necessary to produce one pound of beef, and again this is insignificant beside the 90,000–110,000 gallons of water used in the fabrication of one car.

It also takes 500 gallons of water to provide a daily intake of 2,500 calories of food for one person. This figure is sometimes called the water–calorie ratio.

We cannot alter the amount of water a plant needs and we cannot directly reduce the enormous volumes of water which are used by industries producing useless products. But if it really is the case that we in Europe are using water at three times the rate at which accessible reserves are being replenished, then some definite changes are obviously necessary in our personal ways of doing things, particularly in the way we go about cleaning people and places, and the way we use the products of industry.

17

Washing Machines for People

To make a bath, first build a foundry where the basic shape of the bath is formed by pouring molten iron into a mould. Toxic fumes and heat pour into the atmosphere. Then colour the bath, by a process called vitreous enamelling; where a finely ground suspension of white or coloured glass is sprayed over the iron and then baked in very hot ovens until it forms a smooth glassy skin. Other types of bath are made by vacuum forming oil-based acrylic plastic.

Next make the fittings, usually out of chromium-plated brass. Brass is a mixture of copper and tin, both expensive and increasingly rare metals. Chromium is a rare metal and is bonded to the polished brass surface with flashings of copper and nickel – two more rare metals. Some taps are gold-plated, which is beyond comment.

So simply to instal the basic equipment in the home, we incur a large personal entropy debt, and deplete several rare resources.

Once the bath is fitted, we need materials to keep it clean. These are usually abrasive powders, mixed with bleaches, scents, colouring and antiseptics to convince us that we are cleaner than clean, and that nothing like an ordinary bacterium will ever get near the sparkling surface of the bath enamel. The old Victorian brick sewers under the London streets are now beginning to crumble due to the combined action of the bleaches and other ingredients of waste water.

Then we fill the bath. We pour between fifteen and twenty-five gallons of hot water into the iron and glass container, then we get in, soak for a few minutes and get out. Then the hot water rushes away down the drain.

Now consider the energy needed to heat that water. Imagine three large gas rings burning under the base of the bath.

Depending on surrounding air temperature, the gas rings would be on for about 45 minutes to raise the water to a comfortable temperature.

Now follow the hot water rushing down the drain. Some heat has already been given up to the metal bath, the air of the bathroom and the person in the bath. Then the waste pipe warms up as the water passes on its way to the main drain, and finally the remaining diffuse wisps of heat disperse as total entropy or slightly warm sewer water. All the heat from the three gas rings is now dissipated beyond recall, and has had no function other than to reduce the incidence of chilblains in sewer rats and needlessly to raise the gas bill. The fifteen to twenty-five gallons of carefully prepared fresh water are now mixed with sewage and industrial effluent and flow away beyond recall to ruin the sea-bed.

I measured the amount of water used in a shower lasting three minutes. It was about two gallons. The equipment necessary is simple compared with the cumbersome and expensive iron container called a bath. The shower cabinet can be made of wood and the fittings of the less extravagant of the rare metals. In addition to the five-fold saving of water, there is at the very least a similar saving in heating costs, since fuel is used only while the shower is in use, whereas a bath uses stored hot water which inevitably loses heat to the air however well the storage tank is insulated.

I regret the passing of my bath intensely, since the sense of luxurious languor it produces is marvellously relaxing. But there it is, it has to go. A hot shower is pleasant too and you keep just as clean.

In a Gaian society, baths are out.

18

Washing Machines for Clothes

To wash people, clothes, dishes and places, you can use either of two materials: soap or detergent. Both have a similar cleaning function.

Soap is made by treating fats or oils with caustics. The process uses materials that are in plentiful supply and largely natural in origin. Detergent is an oil-based material made by a large-scale energy-intensive process involving a number of complex molecular manipulations. Soap needs only vegetable oil, caustic and simple technology, and creates no large entropy debt. Detergent needs fossil fuel, quantities of energy and complex technology, and creates a large-scale entropic debt. Soap in used washing water easily degrades to materials which are degradable in the environment. Detergents on the other hand do not, and may have a much more serious and long-lasting effect on the body of the earth organism, even when called: 'bio-degradable'.

There are several ingredients in domestic detergents. Among them may be 'surfactants', or substances which reduce surface tension and allow dirt to be loosened from fibre. One of these is particularly good at removing dirt from clothes. But put as little as six parts per million in river water and it will kill fish by attacking and destroying the oxygen-exchange membranes in their gills.

Another ingredient is phosphate, and although this has been reduced in amount, it can still be present. Phosphate affects fresh water in the following way.

A closed lake is a gradually self-enriching system. The amount of natural nutrients in the water slowly increases, until there is a balance between plant material and animal life. Finally an over-abundance of plant material builds up, until the lake turns into a marsh. This, in cameo, is the natural history of a lake.

(Scientists generate mystification by calling the history first 'oligotrophic', and then 'mesotrophic' and finally 'eutrophic'.)

If man-produced phosphates are released into the water of a lake, they act as food for the plants, speed up the process of plant growth and thus hasten the life and death cycle of the lake.

I have already mentioned 'whiteness' as a commercially based conditioning symbol. In the case of detergents, the symbol has been raised to the level of an art form, and the media present perennially smiling housewives standing in respectful awe at the latest level of whiteness achieved by the latest detergent.

To achieve this dazzling perfection, domestic detergents may contain bleaches, whiteners, dyes, perfumes, enzymes of bacterial origin and other 'building agents', as they are coyly referred to by the manufacturers. Each is made by a separate industrial process with its attendant output of entropy and pollution, and at least one of the bleaches releases Boron into water, which passes through water treatment plants and ends up in river water. Boron can be concentrated by food crops and in quantities can damage the nervous system.

In a Gaian society therefore, detergents are out – unless they can be made by alternative means by low entropy processes and from renewable materials.

So we are left with soap, which was probably discovered by the Romans when they found that the remains of fat and ashes from animal sacrifice rituals, if mixed with dry clay, would take the dirt out of clothes. The ashes were the caustic which saponified or 'soapified' the fat. Nowadays, soap can be more reliably made by mixing caustic with vegetable fats such as palm, coconut or soya oil, so it is not essential to have animals killed in order to wash.

Washing people is no problem. In a shower, for example, quite a small amount of soap is enough, and the multi-coloured detergent-based 'foam bath', together with other grisly chemicals for cosmeticizing water, can be happily abandoned.

The deception wrought by the purveyors of hair-washing chemicals are without equal. Bathrooms have evolved growing polythene forests of bottles containing multi-coloured, scintillating, fluorescing potions to adjust and create images. All contain one fossil-fuel-based detergent. But some contain herbs which do nothing but produce a smell of herbs, others contain ground fishscales which cause the detergent to look pearly, and others are 'medicated' for use on scalps which are undiseased. And some, in a world of acute food shortage, even contain protein for no other reason than that it sticks to the outer surface of each hair and makes it feel thicker. Protein is also supposed to cure split ends. All it does is to glue them together. At least one contains vitamins which are useless to the hair and unabsorbed by the skin; they go straight down the drain.

About a year ago I stopped using all hair-cleaning chemicals, and instead began simply to soak my hair (what remains of it – I am fairly bald) in hot water. For the first month it felt unpleasant, sticky and hard to comb. Finally it changed and now it is in good condition and all traces of dandruff have disappeared. Occasionally, after a session in the workshop, I have to use liquid soap.

Washing clothes is another matter and depends entirely on the type of clothing you wear. I shall return to this point in the section on warmth. I find that soap-flakes are just as effective as detergents for my own clothes, which I wash by hand. But this practice does affect the type of clothes I wear, and in the section on warmth I want to show how changes in washing habits tend to integrate with changes in the kind of clothes I choose.

In fact, I find that one change helps another; for example, the adoption of a vegetable diet makes a change in washing up. Animal fat adheres far more strongly to dishes than does vegetable fat, and I find that hot water alone is usually all you need to wash up with if you are a vegetarian. When it is necessary to use a cleaning agent, instead of detergent I use a bottle of liquid extract of green soap which anyone can buy in a chemist. It is very concentrated and a few drops only are necessary.

The same applies to the cleaning of floors. So although it may seem odd to interrelate very small-scale effects like these, each seems to add to the next in a synergistic, one-plus-one-equals-three process.

19

Water Watching

I watched one of my children brushing his teeth, while he left the cold tap running down the waste pipe. I measured the time he took, then let the same tap run for the same time into a container. He had used about one gallon.

Assume that the population of London all have the same habit, and brush their teeth twice a day. That means that about 16,000,000 gallons of fresh water go uselessly to waste every day. If everyone in that population were to use one toothmug full of water instead, that would amount to about 15,000,000 gallons of water saved.

Wash your hands in a running tap and you use on average 1.7 gallons. Put the plug in, and you use about 0.5 to 0.75 gallons. Use a spray tap and the amount falls to about one pint.

Use a bucket and a sponge for the car, not a hose. Repair all leaking taps. Put a plastic bag containing a quart of water in the lavatory cistern, and each time you flush you save that amount.

Better still, if you live in the country, pee on the land and use no water at all. Some of the molecules of your urine may turn into flowers, which is a pleasant thought. Unhygienic? No, normal urine is a sterile solution of salts; it is the bleaches, deodorants, scourers and disinfectants that are truly unhygienic – to the earth organism.

20
Warmth

We can keep warm either by wearing enough clothes to conserve body heat, or by living in buildings. Eskimos do not heat their shelter and they keep warm by putting on sufficient body fat and clothing. They are, or were, the only zero energy race on the planet. They build their shelters out of ice or wood, they use no fuel to cook with since they eat raw meat, and they do not heat their shelters.

Assuming however that we do not want to live like the eskimo, how can we adapt our clothing to minimize entropy and pollution?

Many people have already decided on an intuitive basis, or because it feels nicer, that they prefer to wear only natural fibres such as wool, cotton or flax. And Gaian theory confirms that natural fibre is a rational choice.

Consider two shirts, one made of nylon and the other of cotton. To make the nylon shirt, oil is taken from the ground and then put through a series of complex energy-intensive industrial processes, until solid nylon fibre snakes out of the dies into tanks of acid. The process is entropic, polluting and dangerous. A few years ago a nylon precursor plant at Flixborough in Britain exploded, killing several workers, wrecking the entire plant and severely damaging homes in five surrounding villages.

To make the cotton fibre on the other hand, the cotton plant first absorbs nutrients and water from the earth and radiation from the sun, and then a relatively low-energy industrial process turned the raw cotton into weaving fibre. To date no cotton plant has exploded and should one do so, it is likely to be a steam boiler accident of far less formidable proportions than the tragic accident at Flixborough.

There is a tendency to write off disasters like this one as someone else's responsibility, but each time we buy a nylon article, we automatically and irrevocably acquire a share in the devastation at Flixborough, as well as in the next accident which will surely happen – quite apart from assuming full responsibility for the entropic polluting output from the nylon fabrication process. There is no way out of this individual responsibility.

Socks are more complicated. I find that woollen or cotton socks wear out at least twice as quickly as nylon. But even so, wool is still the most suitable material in Gaian terms, since it is produced directly from sheep, which are herbivores and produce the fibre solely by metabolizing grass. Sheep are low entropy grass mowers, with a built-in textile factory.

Natural fibres are in accordance with survival in a Gaian age, and artificial fibres are not. So, out with everything except wool, cotton, flax or silk.

The design of clothing has little to do with function. There is a strong commercial conditioning pressure on us all to hide ourselves inside variegated image generators which, it is skilfully suggested, will provide instant success in life, love and occupation.

These conditioning myths woven around clothing have led to the development of a host of unnecessary artefacts. For some reason, related to images of success, class and social acceptability, it is held to be attractive to wear smooth clothing with creases ironed in. Hence we use chromium-plated, electrically powered steam-squirting entropic machines called 'irons' and large wooden and metal machines called 'trouser presses'. We also use specially designed fabrics and fabric processes which enable clothing to be made 'permanently pressed'. All of these complex and expensive machines and processes are totally unnecessary.

Against this, the argument might immediately be raised that in crumpled clothes we would all look unkempt and shapeless. But is someone really nicer to look at if their shape is disguised by sharp edges than if their clothes hang naturally over their body frame?

Nothing is perfect. I still have one dark sombre grey suit left, which I wear on the increasingly rare occasions when I want to delude someone into the belief that I am a respectable and right-thinking person. I call it my 'establishment-penguin-disguise-kit'. I wore it once during the last year. I hope not to wear it next year. It should make a good scarecrow, or rags for cleaning.

The effect of clothing on social relationship is endlessly fascinating. I frequently visit the House of Commons. If I am wearing my penguin-kit and I use my most practised upper-middle-class accent, the police on the gate call me 'sir'. If I am wearing sweater and jeans, I am looked at in disbelief if I introduce myself as 'doctor' and I frequently encounter attitudes of suspicion and studied hostility.

Some restaurants still insist on a collar and tie before admission. If you are not impressed by this authoritarian classmanship, and conceive of a restaurant as a place you visit to buy food, then use the following strategy. Call for a tie, put it on over polo-necked sweater, gain admission, sit down, order food and start to eat. Once eating, take off tie and hand it back to head waiter politely. He will not ask you to leave because you have started the meal and not paid the bill. It is all a question of timing.

On the last occasion I did this with friends, the head waiter turned a mottled magenta and veins stood out on his forehead like water pipes.

If you compare an expensive business suit with T-shirt and jeans, in Gaian terms, the jeans and T-shirt make better sense, since both are cotton and do not need ironing. The rich man with his £300 covering has incurred a larger personal entropy debt: another example of the beginnings of a more logical egalitarianism.

My jeans and T-shirt are also hand-washable in soap and do not need that extraordinary device called a washing machine.

The first washing machine was probably a wooden barrel with a tight-fitting lid fixed to a shaft which was rotated by hand or beast power. Clothes, soap and water were put in the barrel until it was half full, the lid clamped on and the shaft rotated. The clothes were cleaned by sloshing to and fro in the turning barrel.

This simple machine has now been replaced by a noisy, stove-enamelled, chromium-plated, electrically driven, automatically controlled mass of expensive, entropic, polluting and water-wasting machinery which is designed to fail from causes which cannot be put right by the owner. Should the programming unit fail, for example, it is not possible even for the service engineer to repair it, since his training does not extend to a knowledge of switching theory. The switching gear in one example I have seen is inextricably encased in moulded plastic which cannot be disassembled: a throw-away computing device that costs £32.

Washing machines are supposed to relieve users of drudgery. This is partly true, but only if the user finds it necessary to dress in the complicated array of image-adjusters which are offered in the conditioning laboratories of the marketplace, and if he or she is also prepared to work for five days to earn the money to pay for the replacement programming unit.[1]

At first, there were occasions when I found my new clothing embarrassing. Because of my middle-class professional upbring-ing, I found it difficult to turn up in shapeless covering at a meeting of other scientists who were all wearing an 'establishment-penguin' covering. In retrospect I now realize that the embar-rassment was entirely due to my own lack of confidence in what I was trying to do, and once I was more certain, the embarrass-ment disappeared; or nearly. I still have sometimes to withstand the: 'Look what the cat's brought in' expression of the penguins.

To sum up a Gaian attitude towards body comfort, then: use clothes of natural fibres only, which can be washed by hand in soap, and which do not need an iron or a washing machine for maintenance.

Now the body is warm, it needs protection from the elements. What about buildings?

[1] At average rate of income, tax paid, in the UK, 1980.

Shelter originally meant simple weather protection. But in modern times Western technology has evolved from the cave, the yurt, the tipi, the tent and the tree-house, and brought us right up to 1984 well before time by inventing the *standard house*.

Amid standard height, average income, social classes one to four, standardized bread, average intelligence and all the other mechanisms designed to reduce individual choice erected by generations of devoted bureaucrats, there is now a standardized home. In Britain, it is called the 'Parker-Morris' standard. Originally, the motivation behind the idea may well have been to provide a definition of minimum acceptable housing. But it has now degenerated into a highly effective tool for the control and expropriation of individual choice. And from the Gaian standpoint it is a grossly unacceptable structure.

Architect Le Corbusier wrote that a 'home is a machine for living in'. What does the Parker-Morris machine really mean in terms of entropy debt and use of raw materials?

A useful beginning is to evaluate materials we use in terms of the amount of energy it took to make them. If a wooden rod is used to support something, then it is true to say that the rod was nearly all made from solar energy, water, nutrients and materials from the ground. That was how the tree was formed before one of its branches was tooled into the rod. But if a steel bar is used in place of the wooden bar, iron ore had first to be dug from the ground, smelted in a furnace and then formed into an ingot. The ingot then went to a steel mill, where, by other energy-intensive processes, it was rolled and hammered into rod form. The wood was made by the energy of the sun and the iron by the energy of fossil fuel. If the *fabrication energy* and *entropic index* of the wood and the iron are compared, the wood wins.

A brick has to be moulded, fired, stored and transported and each process requires fuel energy. Estimates vary widely as to the amount, but it is probably about 1.6 kWht.[1]

Wood has to be seeded, grown, felled, seasoned, sawn, planed, stored and transported. Suppose then that a piece of wood is cut to the same dimensions as a brick, and, assuming that it can perform a similar support and protective function as the brick, its 'fabrication energy' may be as high as 0.5 kWht. But about 90 per cent of this energy comes directly from the sun and so the entropy of its formation was small.

On the other hand, one hundred per cent of the fabrication energy of the brick came from fossil fuel. The brick kilns also release a large quantity of toxic aerial pollutants, and so the *entropic index* of the brick is high.

To extend the comparison between brick and wood, look at the Parker-Morris 'standard' house, which is a theoretical three-bedroom semi-detached house of 100 square metres floor space.

	kWht
Bricks: 16,000 at 1.6 kWht each	25,600
Steel: 1.2 tons at 13,200	15,840
Glass: 320 ft^2 0.38 tons at 6,277	2,385
Concrete: 12 yd^3 at 630	7,560
Cement: 2 tons at 2,200	4,400
Plaster: 3 tons at 900	2,700
Timber: 4.3 cu m = 151.9 ft^3 at 31.3	4,756
Plastics: 250 lb = 0.113 tons at 45,000	5,085
Paint: 4,700 sq ft (assume £1 per 100 sq ft for all coats) thus £47 at 156.2 kWht/£	7,341
Copper etc: 500 lb = 0.226 tonnes at 15,000	3,390
Miscellaneous:	4,000
Total Materials	83,057
Construction energy (deduced from fuel consumption per £ value for construction industry) estimated to be	19,000
Grand Total (kWht/house)	102,057

[1] One kWht or kilowatt-hour-thermal is a measure of the cost of the fuel necessary to make one kWh or kilowatt hour of energy. One kilowatt hour of electricity will keep a one-bar fire burning for one hour. There are about 4 kWht to 1kWh.

It contains 16,000 bricks, steel, glass, concrete and plastic to a total fabrication energy content of about 83,000 kWht, and after additions for constructional energy tops 100,000 kWht.

A wood frame house of equivalent size and facility may use only 34,000 kWht of fabrication energy. So the Parker-Morris house uses nearly three times the amount of fuel energy in its construction than its wood frame equivalent, quite apart from the entropic pollutants released by the brick, metal and plastics fabrication processes.

We now seem to have a basis for distinguishing 'good' and 'bad' materials.

'Good' means:
1. Low first cost.
2. Long life.
3. Low fabrication energy.
4. Low entropic index.
5. High renewability.

'Bad' means:
1. High first cost.
2. Short life.
3. High fabrication energy.
4. High entropic index.
5. Poor renewability.

On these terms, wood is considerably 'better' than brick.

Other materials can carry an even lower *entropic index* than wood. A rammed earth house, for example, many of which still survive in Britain and the United States, can be built for a fabrication energy cost of about 20,000 kWht. But wood is the most generally available material, it is easy to work with simple tools, and, given adequate preservation treatment, it has an almost indefinite lifetime. It is also considerably more versatile than any other building material and few would deny its pleasing aesthetic qualities.

A widespread use of wood in building is often criticized on the grounds that forests are becoming depleted by over-use of timber. It is perfectly true that the forests are being cut down, but one of the main uses to which those millions of felled trees are put is as newsprint. It is estimated that one issue of an American Sunday paper may use as much as seventy acres of forest. So, as a first move, use less newsprint; and where possible use second-hand wood – or a second-hand newspaper.

One other factor needs to be mentioned in relation to materials: the conditioning power of fashion. For example, we are encouraged to see square, sharp-edged and planed wood as the most elegant. Yet many of our oldest and most durable houses are made of rough-hewn, whole trunk wood. In terms of entropic index, rough wood and trunk wood is more attractive, because sawing and planing may amount to two-thirds of the energy input of machine-finished wood.

I recently saw houses in Norway still being made of hewn trunk wood, and the main tools used there are still the saw, the axe, the adze and the brace. I mention this not out of romantic nostalgia for the old ways as the best ways, but out of the conviction that wood makes better sense in terms of 'good' and 'bad' materials, and low and high entropic indices.

Another way of illustrating a Gaian approach to shelter is to compare methods of decoration.

Most houses have some white walls and some colours, and the easiest way of whitening or colouring a wall is to use a tin of white emulsion paint. But emulsion is made by a high-energy process from very complicated and often toxic oil-based chemicals. It carries an equally high entropic debt whether it is white or coloured. Whitewash on the other hand can be made from lime, salt, rice flour, Spanish whiting, glue and water. Whitewash is cheaper than emulsion, and since its constituents are organic or mineral, and it is made simply by stirring and mixing, its entropic debt is far lower than that of emulsion.

The emulsion is sold on its seductive surface, and durability. It can be washed. But the durability of a paint, white in particular, is really to do with how dirty it gets and how strong the underlying surface is. In ordinary household circumstances, whitewash lasts at least as long as its emulsion equivalent, particularly on ceilings. It smells nice too.

The brightest and most vibrant colours can be obtained from

textiles coloured with vegetable dyes. So there is every reason why a house designed to have a low entropy index could be a feast of beautiful colours and textures as well. It would be far cheaper as well to ornament one's walls in this way, rather than spend money on expensive, super-cover, non-drip lustre-finish plastic emulsions called 'Avocado', 'Mocha' or 'Blueberry'. Such paints should be labelled as unfit for human consumption.

What sort of control systems would a Gaian house have?

There is currently an active debate about the distinctions between High Technology, Alternative Technology, Appropriate Technology and Soft Technology. Agreed distinctions between these titles are lacking and arguments often abstract. In the opening years of a post-industrial society, there would be no point in designing control systems for a house, based on highly sophisticated electronics and mechanics. Conversely, there would be no point in abandoning an efficient technological system just because it was part of high technology. What *can* be done is to isolate a bare description of the operational principle behind a particular device – say, a sophisticated computing element used for control – and then to see how its operational principle can be reproduced by a simpler device of lower entropic debt.

For example, suppose there is a need to sense outside temperature and the strength of the sun so as to control water flow across a solar roof. One currently marketed system relies on a pair of solid-state electronic devices called diodes, connected to an amplifier, a phase-splitter and a power switching circuit. Its production involves all the complex technology of the centralized electronics industries. But an identical function can be carried out with a twisted bi-metal strip, a light cell, and a magnetic switch, the making of which involves only simple electromechanics. The costs are similar, but the first cannot be built or maintained by an individual, whereas the second can.

By the same token it is possible to build a small high-speed wind generator of high aerodynamic efficiency using sophisticated industrial techniques. I have built five and the net result of my research has been to show that they are efficient, difficult to maintain and very dangerous. They also wear quickly and explode in high winds. I now claim the title of Europe's number one *Windmill Breaker*. One high-speed mill I designed and built threw a blade in a gale with a noise like a gunshot. The blade travelled over one hundred feet like an unguided missile and rammed itself nearly a foot into flinty soil.

Several sail mills have now been developed which produce the same order of power as a high-speed mill. They are easy to build, easy to maintain and completely safe. They are bigger than the high-speed variety, but there is no significant wear since they move slowly, and the raw materials used are far 'better' in the terms I have already discussed, since they are mainly wood, canvas and a small amount of iron and aluminium. Also, they do not break.

It was an extremely galling experience to discover by experiment that all my physics, mechanics and aerodynamics had only led me to rediscover that the most suitable design of windmill for a post-industrial age was probably 2,000 years old. Hundreds of them can still be seen working on the plain of Lasithi in Crete!

22

Efficiency, Machines and Work

A house is one sort of machine which will change its nature fundamentally in an age of Gaia; what about others?

The most highly developed machine of all is the internal combustion engine, and its most common variant is the car engine. How suitable will this be for the future?

Engineers define efficiency as the amount of work a machine can extract from its fuel, and this is called its 'thermal efficiency'. A car engine may be only 30 per cent efficient since only that amount of energy in the petrol goes into turning its parts. The remaining 70 per cent is lost as waste heat, pollution, noise and entropy from the cooling water, the engine block and the exhaust.

There is no way that these figures can be much improved, since it is a fundamental truth of the second law of thermodynamics that no device can turn all the energy in its fuel into mechanical work. But in an age where entropy is recognized as the prime difficulty to be overcome, the car engine as it is now constructed will be looked at as highly inefficient.

Entropy not only means disorder from waste heat. It also includes general impact on the earth organism, and so involves other factors which indirectly increase disorder.

To illustrate this point, I am going to compare a car engine with a much older engine from the Victorian era. It is a small single-cylinder gas engine, which I found in a junk-yard and restored. It is heavy, slow-moving and clumsy, but if it is compared with the car engine from a Gaian standpoint, it begins to look more attractive. And if qualities more relevant to entropy debt than thermal efficiency alone are taken as a basis of assessment, then it is no longer obvious that the modern car engine is more 'efficient' than the old gas engine.

Because of its simplicity of design, the Victorian engine is cheap to produce and the fabrication energy of its iron parts may be only one-seventeenth of those of the car engine, assuming that the cylinder block of the latter is part made of aluminium. In addition, some of the old engines have been working for well over seventy years, and a car engine is usually scrap after ten.

The Victorian engine has a lower environmental impact since the industries which supplied its mainly iron and brass parts are overall less polluting than the lead, indium and tin industries which supply just one bearing for the car engine. Its materials show a higher renewability, since iron is one of the most abundant of global reserves, and the other rarer metals used in the car engine are increasingly expensive to mine because of their relative scarcity.

On the reverse side of the coin, the thermal efficiency of the Victorian engine is lower than that of the car engine. A highly tuned racing car engine, for example, may achieve a thermal efficiency of thirty-five per cent, whereas many of the older stationary engines were able to achieve only between ten and twenty per cent. Conversely, no one can copy a car engine even in a well-equipped workshop, whereas given a small iron foundry, a lathe, a power drill and some hand tools, the iron stationary engine could easily be reproduced. Further, the car engine is linked to a sophisticated and expensive maintenance system, while the iron engine needs only oil and the occasional flourish of a spanner. The technology of the car engine could never be wholly under the control of a small group of individuals whereas that of the iron engine could.

Other facts, then, begin to appear as an extended definition of the idea of efficiency. These are:

1. Lowest cost.
2. Longest life.
3. Lowest fabrication energy.
4. Lowest entropic and polluting impact.
5. Materials of high renewability.
6. Thermal efficiency.
7. Replicability.
8. Cheapest maintenance.
9. Simplest maintenance.

I am not proposing a Utopian return to the 'good old days'. It would be dangerous to conclude that some areas of knowledge should, even for some overriding moral reason, be abandoned, and I have already suggested that from this it would be but a short step to another 'burning of the books'. The best and most advanced systems of logic and science can still be married to the most appropriate materials and methods for a Gaian age.

One other idea stems from an extended concept of efficiency: that a structure shall have within it a minimum of man-manipulated molecules. For example, if a plastic pipe can be replaced with an iron or glass pipe, then the need for the complex energy-consuming and entropic technology behind the plastic is removed. Iron and glass tubes can also be made in small workshops under the control of small groups of people, whereas plastic tubing is dependent on large-scale high-energy processes.

Again I am not suggesting that the cars of a Gaian age should be powered by clumsy gas engines fed through glass tubes, but it is clear that designs can change in the direction I have proposed, if the entropy crisis and its effect upon the earth organism is recognized as the primary problem to be overcome.

It may be that in a Gaian age there will be an entropy index applied to each artefact, and that this might lead logically to an *entropy tax*. On this basis, a Parker-Morris standard home would carry perhaps four times the tax load of a wood frame equivalent.

But it is not only the structure of the house which is important, but also how its occupants choose to spend their time inside and outside it.

There are now a number of highly ingenious houses designed to use little energy in their operation. Most run partly on solar power and wind power, and do not draw much energy from centrally generated electricity or from fossil fuel sources. The principles behind these 'autonomous', 'autarchic' or 'self-sufficient' homes are now well established and have been well summarized and developed by a husband-and-wife team of architects: Robert and Brenda Vale.[1]

[1] *The Autonomous House*. Robert and Brenda Vale. Thames & Hudson, London 1975.

Plato wrote that: 'the basic urge of man is to dwell' and this still remains true for our time. But much of life seems to train us to believe that dwelling is all there is to living; that after forty hours of weekly work outside the boundary of the home, we return and switch on automatic reward systems which are designed to restore fatigued minds and bodies.

But there may come a time, not so far ahead in my view, when people may choose to redefine how they work.

At present, work is defined for a very large proportion of people as: *doing what you do not like doing for money*; or, as some political theorists call it: *the sale of labour in a market economy*. Work is going outside the boundary of the home to labour, to earn money, to buy goods which are brought back in through the boundary of the home. But consider for a moment what is brought back in.

Suppose a housewife has worked for a week to earn money to buy beer, fish, pet food, cereal, baby food and a toy. Of the money she spent, the following percentages[2] were probably spent on packaging:

Canned beer	43%
Frozen fish	5%
Pet food	17%
Cereal	15%
Baby food in glass jar	36%
Film-wrapped toy	14%

On average, as much as 20 per cent of retail food prices may consist of packaging costs. Assuming that the housewife's shopping cost £5, then she will have paid about £1 for the packaging, which she has brought in through the boundary of the house. After she has opened the packages she throws them into the garbage can, the contents of which are finally taken out through the boundary of the house again, in exchange for more money paid via the rates to the council garbage removal service.

Put another way, the housewife or her partner may have had to work outside the boundary of the house for over one hour (tax paid at the average national income) in order to buy packaging.

[2] *Modern Packaging*, May 1967.

This obviously suggests that we should buy only unpackaged food, and this is certainly true (see Section 11 above) but it also suggests that the housewife may eventually choose to redefine her work. She may choose, instead of 40 hours outside her home, to work say 20 hours a week to get money outside the boundary of her home and 20 inside the boundary doing work which directly provides needs for which money has not been exchanged; a short circuit of the work cycle.

In the section on bread, for example, I compared the cost of a 'standard' loaf with the cost of a home-produced loaf. It takes about four minutes of muscle-work to grind a pound of wheat into flour and about another 20 minutes to produce a leavened dough ready for the oven. So, it takes 44 minutes of work to save 12½ pence; a poor rate of financial return.

But that amount saved is first of all not taxed. Further, less of a wholemeal loaf is eaten because it is more filling; and it keeps for longer, so less stale bread is likely to be thrown away. There is no packaging paper to add to the garbage can, and the consumer is not forced to eat the poisonous array of chemicals in the 'standard' loaf. The process also helps technological independence, develops survival skill and above all reduces personal entropy debt.

So although 12½ pence saved per loaf is little, by itself, the idea is important, because it leads to a reappraisal of the idea of work.

A bought bottle of wine costs about £1.50, and a home-produced bottle costs 16 pence. I have found that about six bottles of wine can be made for a total work outlay of about thirty minutes, so five minutes per bottle to save £1.34 or over a pound an hour, makes slightly better economic sense. And add to this a saving on the entropy released by the juggernaut which travelled from the vineyard in Spain and the bottling machines of the wine depot.

The do-it-yourself idea has been a splendid move towards individual independence, but now unfortunately, like all other good ideas which tend to free individuals from the pressures of commercialism, it has been cynically exploited by commerce to a point where the skills which the do-it-yourself movement could have enhanced have once again been expropriated by the toymakers. A more accurate definition of what now passes for do-it-yourself might be the following.

First make and put together an article in a factory. Then take it to pieces again and pack each piece in a separate container, add packets of fasteners, and an instruction leaflet, and package the whole.

Then sell the kit for more money than it cost to make the article in the factory in the first place. The buyer pays an inflated price to be deliberately de-skilled.

It is not 'do-it-yourself' but 'live-it-yourself' which is needed. The boundary of the home becomes not just a limiting line around its external wall, but a line surrounding a different way of going about living. High entropy activities lead to a much larger proportion of total loss beyond the boundary of the dwelling, and low entropy activities inside the boundary lead to reduced loss.

The real problem of producing a Gaian dwelling, however, is not only to do with live-it-yourself attitudes; it is to do with planners, building regulations and bureaucrats. A planner can be properly defined by a useful general law: some people get to the top because they do not have enough talent to detain them at the bottom.

A building regulation likewise is an official rule which makes sure that all houses are similar and that no one can build the house of their choice. Clearly some planning laws are needed to prevent people building houses which will fall down and to prevent unscrupulous commercial exploitation of land. But in general, regulations are used by the bureaucracy to diminish innovation, prevent aesthetic experiment and expropriate skills and choices.

It is now possible for someone to take a two-year course in town planning, and then to take a job which gives them total aesthetic and architectural control over the environment of thousands of families. Planners are not in any way elected, yet they can become despots of great danger to the freedom of the individual.

The changes I have so far suggested in connection with dwelling apply just as much to the occupants of an urban apartment as they do to householders in the town or in the country. I also suggest that the changes offer a genuine chance of psychological liberation. The liberation I experience as I increase the rate of change in my own life is to do with a growing sense of independence, from the conditioning power of the marketplace, and from processes which I know perfectly well are anathema to the earth organism.

23

Health

When I qualified as a doctor at a London teaching hospital, I was successfully indoctrinated with confidence in the curative powers of technological medicine; and it was not until I had left the field of clinical medicine to pursue research into vision that I discovered a flaw in that confidence. It was that I was untrained in *healing*, or in the relationship between healer and patient.

I shall never forget my introduction to the hospital. We, the new intake, were all assembled in one room, raring to go, having just finished our pre-clinical exams. A consultant was to address us, and in those days a consultant was next only to God. Finally the Great Man swept into the lecture theatre and we sat in silent awe, waiting for words of wisdom about how to treat the sick. To the surprise and disappointment of nearly everyone, we were told that a consultant liked to be called 'sir' and that we should keep our fingernails clean and wear a suit. Finally the consultant swept out in a flurry of pinstripes and aftershave, and over the succeeding two years most of us were trained not as healers but as medical technicians: people who believed that disease was a fault in an organ or system, which could be put right by altering or removing the organ or system. Sometimes we were shown diseases that were neither infective nor physiological, and these were called 'psychosomatic', as if to suggest that the mind was the causative agent in affecting a part of the body.

I now see illness and health differently. Through language, self-consciousness and present knowledge, we have reinforced the anthropocentric myth that disease is a process which occurs *inside* the boundary of the person; that it is an imbalance in the system *within* the skin; that it is a human biological phenomenon and that it is humans who are central to its genesis.

Western medicine starts with this assumption, and then aims the entire technological juggernaut at its solution. So an ever more complex array of drugs and tools is produced to fortify the illusion that our tool-making capability can create devices to rectify biological faults.

Medical high technology has recently achieved its mythological apotheosis in the heart transplant. Here, between twenty-five and thirty-five university graduates, at a capital cost of over £18,000, combine skills to remove the heart from a dead person and plumb it in the chest of a live person with a diseased heart. The transplant victim gains an average increase in life expectancy of approximately seven months.

Yet the common cold is still the largest cause of short-term disability, and rheumatoid arthritis produces uncountable person-years of agony and despair, and both remain unrelieved. £18,000 would pay for the entire equipment of a Community Health Centre, and materially assist research into colds and arthritis. Or it would pay for several courses of instruction in medical self-help for people who would like to reappropriate the means of health at a grass-roots level.

The cardiac transplant involves the construction of an extensive array of electronic tools and is entirely dependent on large entropic and polluting industries. But the real point is that it has nothing whatever to do with health.

It is a ritualized and theatrical ceremony of medico-technological power. A myth for our times. Dr Barnard really does walk the slopes of Olympus. The heart is no *more* essential to life than are the lungs or the kidneys – life is impossible in the absence of any of these – but the heart is the symbolic centre of the human being, so to transplant it is to perform a miracle and miracles reinforce belief. A heart transplant surgeon makes an LP record and becomes a fantasy success figure, and a doctor who relieves a patient of piles remains anonymous and obscure.

I do not intend to suggest that doctors are not motivated by the wish to relieve patients of their symptoms. There is no doubt at all that, apart from a small proportion of financially greedy opportunists and ordinary criminals, doctors and nurses devote a wholly disproportionate amount of their life to the welfare of others, and I should also admit here and now that I owe my life directly to a number of very highly skilled doctors, surgeons and nurses who managed to repair my abdominal inner tubing, using very high technology methods. So I cannot in any honesty say that the diseased organ directive is ineffective. Clearly it does work. The ulcers in my gut were of unknown cause – psychosomatic, allergic, auto-immune, dietetic, infective: all these causes have been proposed to explain them, but the point is that the doctors and surgeons attacked the problem locally and I am now entirely well. High technological medicine obviously does work in some areas. Also there is no doubt that the global attack on smallpox has almost completely banished this terrible affliction, tuberculosis is well under control and appendectomy saves lives every day. But in their place an entirely different pattern of disease has appeared for which no apparatus, medicine, mechanistic research or surgery will be at all effective. There is now a 'law of diminishing therapeutic returns' which shows every sign of accelerating.

I have called these new afflictions *technogenic diseases*, and the term is meant to imply disorders which arise directly from the high technological way of life. The term certainly includes diseases which are directly caused by industry such as asbestosis, angio-sarcoma of the liver from exposure to vinyl chloride monomer, and chronic bronchitis from urban industrial air pollution. But I also mean it to include a broader group of conditions which are generated by the effects of the uncountable number of new complex man-made compounds to which we are exposed each day. This group will continue to enlarge, and will prove to be ineradicable until there are fundamental changes in the way of life which generates them.

For example, one of the more inaccurately named British parliamentary Acts is the Clean Air Act of 1953. It is often cited as an example of good legislation which significantly reduced the amount of aerial pollution in British cities. This, on the face of it, is true. In a very short space of time, heavily smoking chimneys were banished, the 'pea-soup' opacity of London fogs disappeared and city dwellers could see the sun more often.

But the name of the Act should have been: 'the Clear Air Act', because what it actually succeeded in doing, and I do not want to minimize this real achievement, was to remove some of the carbon and sulphur particles from the atmosphere and so make the air more translucent. What it failed to do was to remove the steadily increasing load of *invisible* poisons.

Every week of the year a new industrial process releases new pollutant gases and aerosols of completely unknown effect. Many are invisible and odourless, and there is no way of recognizing their presence without complex measuring equipment. We are also forced to ingest new liquid and solid pollutants during the course of ordinary living, and, as I have shown earlier, there is no way of avoiding these poisons without completely changing the way we live.

It has recently been suggested that over 70 per cent of human cancer is caused by man-made environmental chemicals, and it is obvious that no one can live in sufficiently isolated hermetic conditions to avoid the effect of these poisons. Similarly, a large proportion of people in Western populations are forced to live and work in conditions which seem almost deliberately designed to produce the maximum of stress and ill-health. Radiation from nuclear weapons and power plants is now global in distribution, there are man-made lead compounds embedded in the ice of the poles and a dreadful ring of dark water surrounds each continental land mass in the Western hemisphere.

If there is really no way of avoiding the influence of this obviously lethal situation, what then is the point of trying to alter our attitude to personal health? What is the practical use of looking at our relationship with the life-force of Gaia if we have already been responsible for an ambient situation which is certain to affect our life-span and health?

No amount of integration with the process of the earth organism will affect the situation if someone develops an acute appendicitis or perforated peptic ulcer. In both cases, unless the services of a skilled surgeon are made available within hours, painful death is almost inevitable. By the same token, a child with an acute lobar pneumonia will clearly be more likely to die if it is not given antibiotics and I have already admitted with gratitude that I owe my life directly to the process of Western technological medicine and to the doctors who used it on me. (To Tom, James and Stanley, thank you. I am alive and well writing this book.)

I mentioned earlier that the first periods of a Gaian age would not be without risk. The health hazard created by the toymakers is an integral part of a one-way process which must certainly result in the virtual extinction of our species in a relatively short space of time. At one end of the process, the industrial-technical process is pouring out a continuous flood of disease-producing material, and at the other, increasingly desperate medical researchers are trying to repair the damage by producing 'technological fix' cures based upon the very technology which produced the disease in the first place: a Catch 22 situation which is bound to worsen without change.

To show how refutation introduces risk, but can improve health in the long term, I want first to look at the consequences of taking an antibiotic, and then to consider 'iatrogenic disease', or disease caused by treatment. Earlier, I used the development of transferable drug resistance in bacteria as an example of intelligent, learning activity in the substance of the earth organism, and one of the themes I have developed is that any threat to stability or continuance generates a self-repair process which may involve feedback loops which take a long time to go through their full cycle. The development and use of antibiotics is a good example of how it is that we exploit a natural process to our ultimate detriment.

Life produces a chemical, an antibiotic, which will destroy some other forms of life. This normally occurs only within the undisturbed natural system of the life process. But then, technical man identifies the chemical, develops and concentrates it, until the fabric of the life process has had to undergo a considerable convulsion to maintain stability.

Antibiotics are made by a large-scale high technology deep fermentation process, requiring very large quantities of fabrication and running energy, and expensive raw materials, all with a high entropic debt. We use antibiotics to relieve sore throats, sore ears and sore toenails; to relieve the symptoms and sequels of the common cold, and to minimize general infections; to treat running noses in humans and pets; to cut short the ordinary pimple and to reduce the time-span of simple conjunctivitis.

On the other hand, antibiotics are also used to save life in acute lobar and bronchial pneumonia, their use has clearly revolutionized surgical technique and they are also vital both to traumatic and general surgery. So there is no realistic possibility of changing our way of health by rejecting them overnight. There would be no advantage in telling a surgeon about to remove an appendix not to use an antibiotic as protection. He would probably refuse to operate; and if he did operate, peritonitis and death would be a much more likely result.

The health of Western populations is now massively at risk. If the methods of technological medicine begin to fail, people will be exposed to dangers for which their bodies have no defence at all, and these will take the form of infection by highly 'learned' organisms with new methods of offence and defence.

There are two ways in which the body can acquire protection against a pathogen, or disease-causing organism. They are called 'active' and 'passive' immunity.

Active immunity is acquired when the body generates protective substances called antibodies, either against a small accidental infection by a pathogen or by its deliberate medical introduction. This form of protection is the most powerful and the most long-lived. Passive immunity is acquired when someone is given laboratory-prepared antibodies, and this is usually less powerful and lasts for a shorter time. It also carries with it another hazard. From birth we are filled with a series of ready-made immune substances giving only relatively weak protection, but as we grow up, we are exposed to an increasingly formidable array of antibiotic-resistant bacteria, which have already 'learnt' the art of survival and are passing it on to their descendants by 'teaching' through the language written in the transferred plasmids I have already described. So if we were to abandon the use of antibiotics suddenly, massive epidemics would sweep through whole populations.

Again we are caught in a self-made trap. By uncritical acceptance of the myth that, given enough 'technological fixes', medicine would gradually conquer all diseases, we have created a situation where the life process has learnt, evolved and developed processes which protect it against the effects of the 'fixes'. It is a situation analogous to the endless competition between the designer of armour plate and the designer of armour-piercing shells.

What can be done, though, is to abandon the use of antibiotics altogether, except in those situations which can be shown to constitute an acute hazard to life or limb. Here then is the first risk. To dispense with antibiotics will undoubtedly lead to an initial increase in pain and suffering, and may prolong illness time. But in the long term, the action must lead to populations with a more powerful and natural immune protection, it will reduce personal entropy debt, and so minimize distortion of the earth organism.

But a return to a real and sustainable health will take a long time. By individual action of this sort from the grass roots, doctors and drug manufacturers will need to get the message that a new breed of patient is emerging: someone who is prepared to ask for health counsel, but who is not necessarily going to accept the automatic use of an unnecessary drug.

All drugs carry some degree of risk from side effects. Even the humble aspirin can produce serious intestinal bleeding. But many of the more advanced and potent preparations have so many dangerous side effects that there is now a relatively new branch of medicine called *iatrogenic disease*, or disease caused by treatment. It is difficult to accept that well-meant diagnosis and treatment by doctors can create disease and death, but the facts are indisputable.

One study[1] shows that one in every five patients admitted to a research hospital acquires an iatrogenic disease requiring treatment. About one in ten of these stem from a diagnostic procedure, and about fifty per cent arise as a complication of drug therapy.

For example, the pharmaceutical industry is competitively engaged in the design of drugs euphemistically called 'tranquillizers', assembling ever more sophisticated molecular configurations. The iatrogenic effects of tranquillizers, or 'mood adjusters' as they are called by the writers of advertising copy, are now well documented, and large sections of the populace are semi-addicted to their regular use.

[1]McLamb, J. T. Huntley, R. R. 'Hazards of Hospitalization'. *Southern Medical Journal* 1967. Vol. 60. p. 469–72.

It is a well-known sick joke among psychiatrists that patients on tranquillizers can be distinguished from others in a hospital waiting-room by their appearance. The patients tend to have mask-like faces, their movements are slow, they may walk with a stamping gait, they may dribble and their speech may be retarded. Tranquillizers can also produce a condition called Akithesia, where the patient's body is continually uncomfortable and where it is difficult for him to keep his limbs still. They may also cause both male and female breasts to lactate, they can create sexual dysfunction and, most serious of all, they can create permanent and untreatable damage to a part of the brain and spinal cord called the extra-pyramidal system. The condition is called Tardive Dyskinesia and may lead to continuous and irreversible writhing movements, grimacing, tremor and protrusion of the tongue.

Iatrogenics is ironically a growing area of medical speciality, and several books have been published about it. One in particular[2] has become a standard work on the subject, and Ivan Illich[3] has extended the idea to consider three main varieties. He refers to 'clinical iatrogenesis', which is the variety I have been describing; and then to 'social iatrogenesis' which he describes as a process where technological medicine actually sponsors sickness by deliberately reinforcing an increasing demand in an already morbid society for the role of patient. The third variety he calls 'structural iatrogenesis', where the health professions are actually destroying the potential of people to deal with ill health in a personal and autonomous way. Illich believes that these three types lead to a 'medical nemesis' in which the dangerous results of diagnosis and therapy lead first to more therapy to cure the bad therapy, then to new institutional decisions to deal with the bad new therapy and finally to the total expropriation of health from people by institutional medicine.

'Nemesis' was first of all a moral idea in mythology; inexorable retribution for arrogance and hubris. Only much later on did the idea become personified in the form of a vengeful female,

[2] *Diseases of Medical Progress.* Moses, R. H. (1969) Springfield. Charles C. Thomas, USA.
[3] *Medical Nemesis.* Ivan Illich. Marion Boyars, London.

who could not be appeased by gifts from those who had offended against the divine equilibrium by taking too much from the world. I accept Illich's view and believe that his concept of medical nemesis as a self-reinforcing cycle is an inevitable consequence of uncontrolled and exploitative technology.

We now have a strong and firmly based legacy of ill health brought about directly by the industrial-technical way of life; and the position cannot be reversed overnight. For instance, as I have already said, antibiotics could continue to be used in acute medical emergency.

We cannot suddenly develop a new and more positive attitude to health, but what can be done is to move towards the reappropriation of health by individuals. This will reduce dependence on the highly entropic industrial process which lies behind technological medicine.

Another important point to realize is that a large proportion of the drugs used at present have no real healing effect at all. They are a product of a mendacious and commercially oriented science, combined with the skills of the advertising industry. Both are deployed to condition doctor and patient alike to the belief that they are effective.

The issue of antibiotics involves life and death, but what about some of the less serious treatments?

Large sections of medicine are a ritualized mythology which exists to maintain belief in the efficacy of a substance, simply because it has been on the books for a long time. Gentian violet, an extract of an Alpine flower, is still painted on diseased or spotty skins, not because it has any curative value – it is in fact a skin irritant and mild antiseptic – but because it is an absolutely fantastic *colour*. It looks like strong medicine. Had it been colourless it would never have been used. Any curative action of the dye is through the eye, and belief in it is a belief in magic.

What was once a relatively harmless display of bright colours and pungent flavours, however, has now degenerated into a ritual whereby chemicals of much stronger and stranger effect are deployed to keep ever more sophisticated and aware patients believing in the power of the medical magician. There are drugs to aid sleep, cure depression, relieve stomach acidity, suppress coughs and alter menarches and menopauses.

There are hormones in orchestrated plenty. Relief from all tribulations and anxieties is promised by a plethora of tranquillizers. There are mood uppers and downers. Wounds are sterilized and healed by magic plasters. And instant death is promised for all pathogens.

Illich refers to the expropriation of health by technological medicine and this is the way it is done. Patients and doctors are carefully conditioned to believe that regular exposure to this multi-coloured armamentarium of chemical rubbish is the *only* way to health, and that rejection is tantamount to disaster. Patients are rarely encouraged to cope with their own symptoms, to learn to distinguish between the serious and the trivial, to lessen their dependence on magical elixirs.

The expropriation of the means of health is now steadily eroding knowledge of the self-healing power of the body. The body is in many ways a Gaian microcosm and, like its parent organism, it is a compact and complex mass of intelligent, self-repairing systems which, left to themselves, can usually restore health – provided that the leaseholder has enough confidence to leave it alone. The methodologies of technical medicine specifically attack that confidence, and encourage the belief that the way to health is by regular machine scrutiny and administration of the latest pharmacological nostrum. Dependence on pills and machines is sold as a virtue, and both independence and a need for self-cure are redescribed as the qualities of a 'bad patient'.

It is rarely admitted that the nostrum may have crippling side effects, or that the body may learn to reject its effect so that higher and higher doses become necessary. When a drug ceases to be effective it is automatically assumed that this was a fault of the drug. So a new drug is produced involving one more entropic debt. Finally the new drug becomes ineffective as well, and so the law of diminishing returns comes into operation, increased entropic debt results and a massive industrial-scientific system is linked to a failing sequence of events. Because this process is already obvious to the commercial drug pushers, a massive sales campaign is mounted to make sure that there is enough consumption of the drug-before-the-next to ensure that the self-destructive, profitable and largely non-therapeutic process continues.

Every six to eight hours between 50 and 80 per cent of the adults in Great Britain and the United States swallow a prescribed medical chemical. Many of these patients ingest an old or contaminated batch, and others may swallow a counterfeit drug. Yet others will take more than one medicine in dangerous combination, and some will receive an agent from a syringe which is already contaminated with disease organisms.[4] Failure of medical treatment was once a personalized affair between patient and physician and was recognized as a failure of trust or ability. Today a maximum permissible drug culture has developed to maintain the myth of cure by drugs and machines.

Complex chemicals in pretty capsules and packed in elegant boxes are available for the adjustment of any mood between nirvana and incipient suicide. One in every ten nights of sleep in Great Britain is drug-induced. In the United States 19 per cent of women and nine per cent of men take a medically prescribed tranquilliser in any single year;[5] and the total sales of mind adjusters make up 31 per cent of the total drug market.[6]

The technical medical process has evolved from a prime curative function into a ritual of technological ingenuity and power which often acts in direct opposition to the maintenance of health. The myth masters of technological medicine have not only expropriated the skills necessary to maintain health, but encouraged the belief that relief can be obtained only from the magic chemical factories. Indeed, they have gone so far as to produce deliberately frightening and cautionary myths to threaten dissidents.

For example, business executives who live an unusually unhealthy life, spending much of their time sitting down, eating, smoking, drinking, competing and worrying, are encouraged to have what is called a 'check-up'. During this process, usually

[4] This is taken from *The Limits to Medicine* by Ivan Illich. Marion Boyars, London 1976. The author gives the medical references from which the statement is made.

[5] Dunlop, D. M. 1970. 'The Use and Abuse of Psychotropic Drugs'. *Proc. Roy. Soc. Med.* 63.

[6] Goddard, J. L. 1973. 'The Medical Business'. *Scientific American* 229. 161–6.

performed with the use of computers and for profit, clinical examinations, blood-fat tests, X-rays, tappings, thumpings and generalized probings are performed, with the sole intention of frightening the daylights out of the customer so that he will want to comply with the advice he is to be offered. But the operators of the scheme know that the client in fact cannot comply with the advice. He will return to the same lethally unhealthy way of life. So they have knowingly created a situation wherein the client will be more likely to end up as a patient, because they have added fear and dependence into his make-up. All that is missing from the process is background chanting, joss sticks and magic symbols.

It is possible to reject this sort of conditioning. People who know themselves to be healthy can reject *all* drugs and treatment based upon technological medicine. But I have to admit that I am not yet confident enough of this statement to be sure that I shall muster the necessary courage to act accordingly in the face of a serious disease. But at the age of fifty I now feel fitter than I ever felt before, and although I cannot *foretell* the future, I believe that I can *affect* my medical future by this belief: that the act of belief in the possibility of autonomous cure may be enough by itself to reduce the likelihood of disease in the future.

I began by stating that it was limiting to think of disease as a process occurring just inside the skin. The consequent idea that disease causation is referable to the earth organism is now a source of great benefit to me. Each time I return to contemplation of the belief that I am an inseparable part of the earth organism, I feel very much more than intellectual pleasure: symptoms actually vanish and aches ease. The thought that it is within my own choice to rediscover and develop this relationship is a powerful source of health. Thought itself seems to act like a curative draught, but the effect is the reverse of narcotization. This inward conviction is a sustainable source of health provided that I actually live by the process of continuing change and refutation I have been describing and do not allow the process to become theoretical only. Here then is a balance of opposites; health can be achieved by a course of action and risk which is consistent with minimum damage to the earth organism, but only if each necessary change is lived out to the full. It is, I suppose, really a process of continuous internal revolution.

Personal health then can develop from a central understanding of the unity between self and Gaia. Confidence in this belief can create an internal conviction which can genuinely strengthen the self-stabilizing and self-repairing systems of the physical body. It can also affect attitudes to pain.

In the United States, about 20,000 tons of aspirin are consumed annually, and this amounts to 225 tablets per head of population per year.[7] Aspirin is the name for Acetyl salicylic acid which can produce stomach bleeding and duodenal irritation. It is absorbed into the bloodstream as a sodium salt, where it is alleged to exert a pain-relieving effect. Even orthodox pharmacological texts refer to this ability to relieve pain as mild. But is even this mild relief real? It seems to be another example of the medical institution offering a chemical solution for a symptom which may be part culturally based. Any pain severe enough to cause a person to take aspirin is in fact probably a pain which aspirin cannot relieve (though this statement must except the specific effect of salicylates on rheumatoid arthritis).

It seems absurd to say that when you bang your thumb with a hammer the sensation created is a cultural phenomenon: it is obviously a mixture of pain, fear and anger. But there is no doubt that in China patients undergo major abdominal surgery without the anaesthetics that are normally used in the West. Many Western doctors have witnessed these operations. If it is assumed that the brain and nervous systems of Chinese and Western patients are similar, then the only possible conclusion is that the Chinese are reacting to pain differently.

When I was suffering the illness I have already referred to, I developed a general peritonitis following surgery. I had no idea, even as a doctor, that such pain could exist. During one night, the worst of my life, the whole universe turned into pain. The walls and ceiling of the ward were pain, the bed was pain, every smell was pain, every touch and sight and noise was pain. There was no other experience and no glimmer of relief. And I simply

[7] Brecher, E. M. *et al. Consumer Union Report on Licit and Illicit Drugs.* Boston, Little, Brown. 1973.

could not make anyone understand how terrible the experience was. Eventually I did manage to get through to a nurse, and I was given drugs. Once I had communicated across the harsh gulf of the darkened ward, my whole reaction to the pain altered in kind and I could just tolerate the experience although the 'pain' did not diminish. Shortly afterwards I was being tended by a nurse with beautiful Elizabethan eyes. I was in a poor physical state and the sight of my condition made her weep. Her tears altered my whole reaction to my suffering. Her compassion was the most powerful analgesic it is possible to imagine.

Pain is partly suffered out of loneliness: I felt I was in the midst of a hard, chromium-shining, uncaring institution. But I had really only discovered something which has been known to other cultures for thousands of years.

From my days as a hospital doctor I remember one patient who had terminal cancer, and who was suffering from pain which no amount of drugs would relieve. Eventually, he was subjected to a leucotomy, an operation which cuts some of the connections between the front and the middle parts of the brain. I remember asking him how the pain felt after the operation, and he replied that it was exactly the same, but he smiled easily as he spoke. His reaction to the pain had changed. The pain was still there, but he did not suffer from it.

Nobody needs a leucotomy after hitting their thumb with a hammer, but the principle behind that patient's change, and my own small experience, is something I believe can be developed. Pain, or the reaction to pain, can be changed by the relief of loneliness, by knowledge of the compassion of others. What Illich calls 'the total medicalization of culture' has trained us to demand that pain be done away with by a chemical means, and not by exposure to real care, real love and real compassion.

The word for pain has quite different meanings in different languages. In some it includes ideas of sorrow, grief, anguish, shame, and guilt; in others it refers also to toil, endurance, hunger, mourning or confusion.[8] This is a further indication that reactions of individuals will differ across cultures.

I have found that it is possible to distance self from pain in

[8] *The Limits to Medicine*. Ivan Illich. Marion Boyars, London 1976.

such a way as to be more in control of its effect. Once control is achieved, one can choose to grimace and cry out or to remain quiet and to contemplate the sensation in a more detached way. Again it would be arrogance to say to an arthritic, or to someone undergoing an acute abdominal emergency, why don't you contemplate the pain instead of taking drugs? But the effect of the technique is real and lasting.

So pain really does have a cultural and social component. Hence the seeds of much pain relief lie in cultural and social attitudes too, and not solely in the hands of the designers of analgesic drugs. The Chinese have a saying about sharing: 'The truth is communicated between unique pairs.' The unique pair in relation to health, disease and pain is that of patient and healer. No drug can supplant the relief which can be found in a true rapport created between the two.

Any move towards reappropriation of a different way of health is bound to suffer a long crisis of confidence. Our conditioning may take years to eradicate. And the technogenic diseases will continue to increase until such time as the system which produces them is changed.

But it is possible in the midst of this conditioning to re-evaluate the way we want to maintain health, and so to begin to take the definite risk of rejecting as much of the mechanics of institutionalized health as possible. By so doing we shall materially reduce personal entropy debt because we become independent of the medical-industrial complex, and also because we will begin to relate health not to doctors and institutions, but to our relationships and the way we live within the boundaries of the earth organism: the reconnection of all our body systems to the broader envelope of one body-mind-individual-life-process system.

This is not an attempt to convert health into a mystical state. It is no more than the most pragmatic of approaches, recognizing the nature of a fundamental error, and altering our way of seeing so that the error is rectified.

Doctors have had the most privileged of educations, and it is therefore not their task to sell their skills for profit or prestige. It is their duty to give them away to those who need them. I shall return to this point in the section on education.

24

Energy and Myths

Earlier in this book I described the flow of energy through the substance of Gaia, and described energy itself as an 'idea of something' which can be converted or transformed. Two forms of this something are directly available: transformed or stored solar energy on the earth's surface, and stored solar energy underground in the form of coal, oil and gas. I also used the example of a bonfire burning as entropy; and suggested that the life process by itself tends to reduce disorder, or maintain it at a reasonably constant level, and that man can also reduce disorder; but that in so doing, man releases a far greater amount of disorder to the planet elsewhere, in the form of pollution, waste heat and unusable waste. I developed the idea of the solar drive chain, and showed that we were the only species ever to have removed our dependence upon it, by using fossil fuel. I also suggested that there is no such thing as an energy crisis and that there is enough coal, oil and gas to continue our current lifestyle until such time as we are finally submerged in a swamp of entropy.

In the section on shelter I introduced the idea of *fabrication energy* as the amount of energy it takes to create an object, and I suggested, as an example, that it takes some one to six kilowatt-hours-thermal[1] to make, mould and fire one brick. Every artefact has its fabrication 'price tag', and it follows that any move towards Gaian living has to involve an examination of this price tag in full detail, since the real 'crisis' is not to do with energy, but the entropy of the industrial process.

[1] A good clear introduction to energy and its forms is a CSE schools textbook, *Matter and Energy*, by N. E. Savage and D. S. Wood. Routledge & Kegan Paul, London 1972.

So, as well as reworking our approach to the primary requirements of food, warmth, shelter and health, we need also to look in detail at all the other artefacts we use and to see whether these can be changed to reduce personal entropy debt.

When the first imperialists stole land from foreign native populations, they used as one of their currencies of exchange shiny glass beads; native populations were induced to believe that shine and glitter were indications of value. A similar confidence trick has been perpetrated on the car buyer, and although it is possible to pay for one car an amount of money which would buy a row of six small terrace cottages, and for another a sum which would just buy lunch for two in a London restaurant,[2] similar conditioning glitter adorns both machines. The glitter is designed into the structure of the car for much the same reasons of deception as governed the use of beads as a medium of exchange. When one looks closely enough, in fact, only a small proportion of the structure of a car has anything to do with transport. Most of the metals and plastics used are to do with ritual, and with images of class, wealth and prestige.

Think of cars as adornments to express social discrimination: a Rover for the county middle class, a Mini for the worker; a Rolls-Royce for the senior director, and Ferrari *machismo* for the pop star; a Daimler for weddings and to carry the dead in blackness and in silence.

We take raw materials from the earth to create technological fantasies of chariots and fairy-tale carriages. A car is a mobile shrine.

To illustrate the way the components of a car contribute to personal entropy debt, I shall analyse the example of the bumper, on the face of it the most practical of accoutrements.

A bumper once did indeed have the function of protecting the bodywork from damage. Now it is only body decoration. Look at how it is made.

First, its shape is drawn on paper. Then the shape is hand-carved in a specially hard plaster. The plaster shape is copied in solid steel, using a large three-dimensional duplicator cutter,

---

[2] In 1978 one could buy a 1977 Rolls-Royce Corniche at £30,122; or a 1959 British Leyland Mini at £22.

and from the convex solid steel shape a concave fitting copy is made. The paired shapes are then bolted into a large hydraulic press and a ribbon of steel sheet fed in between them, and stamped. Each bumper, after stamping, is cleaned and fettled before being carried to the polishing and metal-plating plant where it is to acquire its essential appearance: glitter.

At the plating plant it is buffed and cleaned preparatory to being plated with chromium – which is very bright but a bad covering for steel because it does not adhere strongly to it. So the steel pressing is given a flash coating of copper, then a thicker coating of nickel, and finally the coating of chromium. Chromium, copper and nickel are all relatively rare metals and large quantities of electrical energy are necessary to bond them on to the steel surface.

The now glittering bumper is then fixed to the body of the car. This is often done in such a way that it is in direct contact with the bodywork, so when the bumper is hit and bent, the bodywork is also damaged – negating the apparent purpose of the whole operation.

The car owner is now trained to clean, polish and protect the shining bumper – washing it with special car shampoo, polishing it with chromium polish and finally lacquering it with a transparent varnish to protect not its function but its shine.

Suppose, after all this, that the owner hits a lamp post and dents the bumper. It is removed, thrown away and replaced. The replacement may cost between £7.40 and £178. Assuming the replacement bumper cost £65, an average wage earner might have to work for nine days to earn enough money to replace a part of his car *which has no function*. A more insane situation would be difficult to imagine. A massive entropy debt has been acquired to buy a structure which now lies rusting on a scrap heap.

One bumper does not make a motor car, but the story is one indication of how we need to retrain our commercially conditioned heads towards choosing a more suitable car.

It is also instructive to compare, say, a Rolls-Royce Corniche with a Mini Minor on a basis of raw material usage. The Rolls-Royce weighs nearly three times as much as the Mini and an average car may contain 1,400 lb of steel, 280 lb of cast iron, 10 lb of lead, 30 lb of aluminium, 80 lb of rubber, 72 lb of plastic, 30 lb of zinc and 50 lb of glass.

The average occupancy of a car entering central London is just over one person per car, so assuming that the Rolls-Royce owner and the Mini owner are both single occupants for 20,000 miles per year, not only is the Rolls owner in possession of a very much larger mass of fabricated raw material, but he burns in addition some 928 extra gallons of petrol, for no purpose related to mobility or transport.[3] The heat released from 928 gallons of petrol would centrally heat three small houses for one year. It is obvious that the Rolls owner has incurred a far greater personal entropic debt, and so does far more damage to the earth organism.

It follows again that this way of looking at artefacts forms an entirely logical basis for a more egalitarian society. We can enlarge the idea of equal shares for all, by including the idea of 'equal entropy debt' as well.

The individual body parts of a car are also overstyled to a point where they incur quite unnecessary pollution and entropy debts. A car wing, for example, is basically a box structure to keep grit and water from flying off the wheels, but it has now turned into another cultural totem of success, godliness and sex. Streamlining makes very little difference to the performance of a car at legal cruising speeds. Yet car wings of grotesque quasi-aerodynamic form are sculpted not to make the car travel more efficiently, but to allow the driver the fantasy of speed in a chariot of the technical gods, and to surround him with a steel surrogate for a thigh. About the only individual achievement left for a virility-oriented male in the city is that of overtaking another car, so a car of aerodynamic shape becomes basically a boulevard theatrical prop, even when it is driven at five miles per hour down the King's Road in Chelsea to impress a female pedestrian audience.

Indeed a 'sports car' can be defined as a car of similar performance to its saloon equivalent, which carries fewer people in conditions of relative discomfort, less economically and for a

[3] Assuming a mileage per gallon of 14 for the Rolls-Royce and 40 for the Mini. Averages selected from *What Car*, March 1977.

greater first cost (that is, greater use of raw material) per passenger.

As I write this I have just finished making a car with bodywork entirely constructed from wood. It is based upon Mini components, panelled in marine plywood and varnished. It looks like a box on wheels. It drives well, carries people, and will, if revarnished every so often, last for at least a century. The only problem I can see looming is woodworm or deathwatch beetle, and so I have christened it *The Woodworm Express*, a title which raised a few eyebrows when I came to register it at the Department of Transport. Fortunately some bureaucrats retain an excellent sense of humour.

In a just society, public transport would largely replace the car, but given the present unjust situation, there is no point in telling an elderly person in a remote country district to 'take a bus' if there are no buses. A car is still sometimes essential.

But now I want to take a look at some other high technological machines which have reached truly splendid levels of absurdity.

There is very little evidence that brushing the teeth has any effect at all either on tooth lifetime or on dental caries. Yet a complex and entropic industry exists to supply brushes, pastes and powders. It has now reached its apotheosis: the all-electric, forearm-muscle-replacing, multi-headed, multi-coloured toothbrush.

Teeth rot and fall out from a variety of causes and few of these are influenced by the devices and potions offered to the consumer-tooth-cleaner. There are certainly other factors: who your ancestors were is important, and what you eat is basic – tooth hygiene agrees well with the suggestions for change in diet in the section on food.

For example, in Mönchweiler, a town in the German Black Forest, a dentist started an experiment with the co-operation of parents, bankers and the Mayor. About 300 children were involved and two groups were compared. One ate whole bread, fresh leaf and root vegetables, raw nuts, unheated milk and fruit.

The other ate anything they wanted. In the group which followed the dentist's advice, one- to three-year-olds showed a 100 per cent decline in caries, three- to six-year-olds an 86.5 per cent fall, and ten- to fourteen-year-olds 36.5 per cent.[4]

No professional forgives a colleague who makes him look like an idiot, reduces his income and demystifies his skill. The dentist was sued and threatened with disbarment by his professional dental association. But after media exposure and public support he eventually won his case.

The British Dental Health Foundation published a report in 1972 in which it referred to an epidemic of tooth decay and stated that 25 per cent of five-year-old children would wear dentures before they were twenty. These sad statistics are almost certainly related to diet, and in particular to the consumption of refined sugar.[5] They are also related to magnesium deficiency, which may be one consequence of eating white bread.

To counteract this apparently growing tendency towards generalized tooth rot, many governments, in spite of very considerable public protest, have introduced fluoride into drinking water. Fluorides are supposed to prevent tooth decay, but evidence[6] shows that decay may be only partially reduced or delayed in onset. The addition of a powerful chemical to centralized water supplies is an entirely non-democratic action and is another example of the expropriation of health by a state in the face of evidence for the existence of other factors.[7] It is a case of shutting the door after the horse has bolted.

One electric toothbrush I examined weighed one pound ten ounces, complete with batteries. Nestling in a transparent green polystyrene box is the vibrator unit and four separate brushing heads. It is designed for a family, and the idea behind the four heads is to encourage the notion that togetherness is to do with group electrical consumption. The actual purpose is to condition consumers to use a totally unnecessary machine in groups. Over

[4] Reported by Bunyard, P. *Journal of Soil Association*. Jan. 1971. p. 15.

[5] Yudkin, J. 1963. *Lancet*.

[6] *Public Health Report No 22*. Her Majesty's Stationery Office.

[7] Hart, H. M. (1969) *Lancet*, p. 99. Clear, T. L. *et al*. Diabetes, Coronary Thrombosis and the Saccharine Disease. J. Wright & Sons, Bristol. Sinsters, G.B. *World Medicine*. March 1969.

one and a half pounds of polystyrene, nylon, polyvinyl chloride, copper, iron, nickel and brass are assembled for this purpose, and the acreage of the electric-toothbrush factory permanently covers valuable agricultural land with concrete.

The electric toothbrush is an easy target. I have two tooth-brushes in front of me. One has a transparent handle with nylon bristles. Microscopic examination of the bristle tips reveals that they are sharp and ragged – specifically designed to damage tooth enamel and to tear the gums. The other comes from a Buddhist monastery in Thailand. It is a four-inch stick of wood, sharpened at one end to act as a tooth-pick and teased out into wooden bristles at the other. The nylon brush was made from fossil fuel and the wooden brush is made from solar energy and is disposable. The nylon brush carries a high entropic debt and the Buddhist brush a low one, since it uses *no* raw material which would not otherwise be burnt or subject to decay or re-cycling.

Toothpaste was originally designed to be a mild polish and was made from chalk, refined soap, essential oils and water.[8] Now it is made from fossil-fuel-based detergents, humectants, emulsifiers, flavouring agents, colouring agents, disinfectants and preserving agents – *none* of which has any function to do with cleaning teeth and *each* of which is the completely superflu-ous product of a separate entropic industry. Many of the new substances have also been tested on animals by painful exper-iment for no other reason than to provide manufacturers with legal protection.

The industry which has grown up around the doubtful habit of tooth brushing is a good example of how talented men and women and conditioned consumers can reach an uneasy consen-sus to consume energy and raw materials for no functional reason.

The same goes for electric carving knives, electric shoe polish-ers and electric hair curling machines, all of which are sold on the shape of the container and a promise of success and approval rather than any real function that the machine might perform.

[8] *Recipes, Formulas and Processes*. G. D. Hiscox. Crushy Lockwood, London 1910, 1959.

If products without function are made and consumed by general consensus, then they must clearly have some other role in society than a functional one.

Nobody has ever decided what myths are and what they are not. Some believe that they are stories told about symbols which connect people to nature and the universe. Others think that they are dogma designed to reduce paradoxes and smooth out ambiguities; and there are yet others who assert that they are meant to legitimate existing social orders, and to validate power structures in social groups such as the family or the state.

Robert Graves has expressed his opinion[9] that myths attempt to answer the sort of awkward questions children ask, such as: 'Who made the world? How will it end? Who was the first man? Where do souls go after death?' So they deal in mystery as well.

Myths are altered by successive generations, and no doubt this is partly to conform with social changes. But if their function is the legitimation of the existing social order to validate authority – then it is interesting to look again at some of the technological structures we have been conditioned to accept as if they were symbols of a technological myth.

Such is the force and skill of the advertising which sells some of the more extreme artefacts that it becomes almost a question of faith to acquire the latest and shiniest gadget as soon as possible. So to acquire becomes the equivalent of self-protection against the charge of heresy rather than avarice. We are not simply 'keeping up with the Joneses' but stocking the house with devices to show *belief* in the industrial system. The house and its occupants are protected from harm if the correct set of talismans is displayed. The bumper, the electric toothbrush and the throwaway razor are acquired to reduce anxiety, by publicly declaring faith in the high technological myth. Again, this behaviour could be traceable to the idea that the industrial society has deskilled people to a point where to do without an artefact even if it has no function is to put oneself at risk.

To rip the top away from the soft-drink can thus not only satisfies an inner destructive urge, but is another behavioural

<hr>

[9] Robert Graves. Introduction to *Larousse Encyclopaedia of Mythology*. Hamlyn, New York, London.

pattern showing conformity. Technocrats sell the idea that to tear and crush the precious metal and to swallow the undrinkable contents, is a celebration of the machine and a legitimation of the power of the technologies behind it. The new aristocrats are the machine makers and it may not be too long before they adopt holy orders.

In the face of a mythology which has got out of hand, therefore, premeditated heresy is a good idea. In the sections on Food, Warmth, Shelter, Health and Energy, I have been suggesting a basis for this heresy.

I have expressed my heresy in the mythological guise of Gaia, one of the most ancient and powerful of all the Gods. She first created the universe, then the first race of Gods, and then she gave birth to the human race. Her position in Greek mythology was central. As earth mother she was held to be the bestower of all fruitfulness and abundance. Even after her sons the Titans had been defeated by Zeus, so establishing the Olympian rule of the patriarchal gods, it was still the practice to invoke her powers of creation in ordinary human ceremonies.

I have used the myth of the goddess Gaia to express the idea that we are an integral part of a single, intelligent life-form which acts like an individual. I have tried to show how it is that we can never separate ourselves from this life-form, despite our delusions of dominance and control, because should we succeed in doing so, we would be committing an irreversible act of mass suicide: as if an arm tried to exist separately from the body. But although I have suggested an alternative myth to the ritualized symbology of the machine society, I do not want it to be thought that I have been presumptuous enough to take on the role of myth-maker. What I am suggesting is perhaps no more than a means towards the reacquisition of ancient knowledge, that could bring us back from the brink of extinction to the prospect of an infinitely sustainable future. And I foresee as a consequence the redevelopment of faculties which we once had as a commonplace and have now suppressed – this is the optimistic conclusion I want to explore in Part Three of this book.

The machine has also taken over festivals which once had a religious basis.

Christmas was once a festival to celebrate the birth of Christ, and it is almost a truism to say that it has become no more than a short spasm of premeditated over-consumption. I see this extravagant spending spree as another ritual celebration of the machine, held to induce people to buy goods into their homes as visible signs of success in commercial-technological terms. A plethora of disposable and largely useless materials demonstrates that the consumer and the technical-commercial process have both made it without disaster to the end of another year. The polystyrene angel at the apex of the tree becomes a symbol of the validation of high technology: it is reassuring us that there are still factories able to expel a continuous stream of disposable plastic angels. God is still in the machine and all is well.

There is no need to dwell on the clouds of entropy and pollution which inevitably drift away from homes during this annual celebration of the machine.

The saddest emblem of the whole ritual is the Christmas tree. Each year hundreds of acres of land are sown with seed and each year in Britain alone some 13 million trees are torn from the ground. Their roots are cut off or boiled, and the dying trees are jammed into wooden blocks so that they will stand vertical. They are then taken into our homes, not for any celebration of the tree, not for any belief in growth or renewal, but to be turned into symbols of the machine, our power over nature. Accordingly, they are adorned with the maximum possible weight of metal and plastic. The once living green of the branches is coated in *aluminium* tinsel, *copper* wire, *electric* lights and *plastic* bubbles until the game is over and the corpse is thrown out of the back door.

An idea for a Gaian Christmas might be to build a metal and plastic tree – of the greatest possible ugliness – and then to plant a rapidly growing creeper at its base, and watch the living green obliterate the metal.

The age of technological dominance has conditioned us to accept that all other species are in some way legitimately subservient to our needs whether those needs are related to survival or not.

We are properly concerned about human rights, particularly in relation to an emergent global bureaucracy, but we might begin to consider that the other elements of Gaia have rights too.

25

The Rights of Animals

We share a small planet with an uncountable number of species, each of which is a part of the living earth organism. And just as there is communication and interaction between the cells, organs and systems of the human body, so is there communication and interaction between the species of Gaia. But interaction between the parts of a balanced whole enforces limits on the activities of each part. In the body, for example, each organ has a particular function within the whole. The kidney has the function of removing waste from the blood, and it is supported by the physiological activities of the rest of the body. It is not, in the absence of disease, attacked by the other body systems, it is supplied with a suitable milieu for its function. Similarly, in the ecosphere, the species to some extent protect each other by creating mutually suitable conditions. Obviously, there is competition and predation as well, but mutual aid and mutual provision underlies the whole.

We have the apparently unique ability to describe and to be aware of all these forces and interactions around us. And so, automatically, we assume responsibility for their continuance. It follows therefore that we should ascribe rights to the other parts of the earth organism. What are these rights?

They arise from the fact of presence. Viruses, bacteria, protozoa, arthropods, vertebrates, primates and man have all been present for a very long time. Therefore all have a 'right' to be there, by virtue of existence and occupancy.

But a virus has to remain a virus, a fly is always a fly and a lion has to remain a carnivorous hunter. It is only we who have free choice. We can freely decide to become farmers, doctors, murderers or Gaians. Choice and the knowledge of this choice automatically implies an acceptance of responsibility, since we possess in full detail all the knowledge, skills and tools to do exactly what we like on a planetary scale. We have the capability to move mountains, drain lakes and alter the fauna and flora of the globe, at least for a limited period of time. We also have the total ability to create an infinitely sustainable symbiosis with the forces of Gaia – if we want to.

But we show little recognition of the rights of other forms of life, and our attitude towards them still remains largely dominating and exploitative. The bibliography of our depredations is massive and needs no detailed repetition. We *know* that we are over-farming the land, we *know* that we are inexorably corroding the green pelt of the planet with a rain of lethal chemicals. We are also in no doubt that this process will eventually stop, and our belief in the power of the old science and technology to provide enough 'technological fixes' to prevent the slide into a post-industrial dark age is waning. So it may seem highly theoretical to start at this point discussing the rights of other life-forms in full view of a self-inflicted chemical Armageddon. It seems absurd to worry about the rights of a cabbage.

But it is precisely by looking at this issue of the rights of other life-forms that it is possible to begin to develop new attitudes to assist the move towards a more optimistic age.

In the first part of this book I sketched the way in which the Gaian organism remains stable, and how our activities act directly against that stability. A sustainable future is no longer a question of moral values or condescension towards nature. Each part of the earth organism is causally linked to the process of solar energy absorption, growth, death, decay and rebirth. This is the first and only principle, and this is the way the planet *does* work. Nothing we have achieved has in any way altered our basic dependence on this. It is only the toymakers who have broken away from this sequential set of laws, and *imagined* a separate and machine-based existence.

If therefore we do genuinely want to evolve a sustainable life-style, we must begin to nurture every part of the earth organism, not for moral or romantic reasons, but because to do so is essential survival behaviour. I strongly believe that, embedded in the necessary changes, there is a new, and more 'moral', ideology which will emerge and stand free of our present anthropocentrism. Perhaps in due time it might amount to a fulfilment of '*La Grande Morale*' of Victor Hugo. He describes this idea:

'It was first of all necessary to civilize man in relation to his fellow men. That task is already well advanced and makes progress daily. But it is also necessary to civilize man in relation to nature. There, everything remains to be done . . . Philosophy has concerned itself but little with man beyond man, and has examined only superficially, almost with a smile of disdain, man's relationship with things, and with animals, which in his eyes are merely things. But are there not depths here for the thinker? Must one suppose oneself mad because one has the sentiment of universal pity in one's heart? Are there not certain laws of mysterious equity that pertain to the whole sum of things, and that are transgressed by the thoughtless, useless behaviour of man to animals? For myself I believe that pity is a law like justice, and that kindness is a duty like uprightness. That which is weak has the right to the kindness and pity of that which is strong. Animals are weak because they are less intelligent. Let us therefore be kind and compassionate towards them. In the relations of man with the animals, with the flowers, with all the objects of creation, there is a whole great ethic (*tout une grande morale*) scarcely seen as yet, but which will eventually break through into the light and be the corollary and the complement to human ethics.'

I am sure that there are 'laws of mysterious equity', and that these involve an unconscious understanding of the process of life which may well have arisen from a collective unconscious stretching back to a time when our ancestors were, by survival need, a unified part of nature. These laws have been distorted and suppressed by the industrial process, so that perhaps like a parody of Pavlov's dogs, we are now more likely to salivate at the thought of a cylindrical metal container labelled with a picture of steaming red beans than at the thought of the beans themselves. But the feeling of relationship to Gaia can be fully released and redeveloped again by a detailed and critical look at other life-forms and the way we make use of them.

Strictly speaking, an animal is an organized being endowed with life, movement and senses; and a vegetable is a plant.

To survive, we need a certain minimum of food, and this inevitably means some destruction to life. Earlier, I made the case that vegetables easily provide a diet nutritionally equivalent to meat, but we still have to kill the plants to eat. We cannot avoid killing in this sense: every time we breathe in, millions of bacteria die in the moisture of our lungs; every time we cook, we kill.

But if animals and vegetables do have a basic right to life, simply by virtue of existence and occupancy of the planet, then it follows that the number of deaths we cause by eating should be kept to a minimum. Again this is not a moral statement, it is related to survival and the need to reconnect our way of life to the cycles of solar absorption, growth and decay. To interfere as little as possible seems to be commensurate with long-term survival.

But we not only misuse animals by eating them, we also abuse them to test substances for potential hazard to ourselves and to test drugs which may have no medical function. By so doing, we reduce animals to the status of mere systems to be exploited. Nowhere is this dominating and manipulating stance more clearly seen than in industrial agriculture, or, as it is less euphemistically known, factory farming.

Eighty-six per cent of eggs sold in Britain are produced by chickens which are confined for life in 12 × 18-inch cages. They are debeaked, defeathered and thrown out for slaughter at about 12 months of age after producing a steady stream of poor-quality eggs. The process produces an unrecyclable amount of manure which is too much for local ground to absorb. It also creates a greatly increased incidence of disease in the animal.[1] When the birds are finally slaughtered, they have their throats cut while hanging upside down from moving hooks on a conveyor belt, to the sound of music. One recent report showed that two out of five birds may enter the scalding tanks at the end of the slaughter line still alive.

Factory farming also creates visual blight, fumes, dust, smell, noise and plagues of flies and rodents. The manure effluent

---

[1] 95 per cent of factory-farmed birds were recently found to contain the virus of infectious bronchitis: *Farm and Food Society*, London.

contains disease organisms dangerous to grazing animals. It generates polluting road traffic, it produces food of lower quality and it is abominably cruel. But it does produce cheaper eggs.

In the section on food I have already made a case against eating meat, so there is no need to dwell on the appalling conditions under which calves and pigs are kept by factory farmers. And it is easy to avoid the 'oven ready' and generally cosmeticized 'Champion's Chunky Chicken'. But it is very difficult to find eggs which have been laid by birds who have led a free and outdoor life. There is a plethora of mendacious labels to sort through – such as 'Farm Fresh' – before one can be certain to have found free-range eggs.

It is better in the end to do without eggs altogether and become a total vegan. A vegan is someone who abstains altogether from animal products, and although I still eat eggs, milk and butter, I fully recognize that the logic of care, responsibility and reverence for life implicit in the vegan position is entirely correct, and I hope before long to have adopted that way of eating.

If we accept that other life-forms of the earth organism do have rights by virtue of existence and occupancy, then it is true that those rights naturally include protection from unnecessary exploitation by another life-form. Yet *toymaking man* has, without genuine need or authority, assumed the right to dominate and to exploit. Perhaps the most scandalous examples are in the field of animal experimentation.

Each year in Great Britain about 5½ million animal experiments are performed, fully licensed by the Home Office. Only 1½ million of these are for medical purposes. The remaining 4 million, many of which undoubtedly involve suffering, are for commercial and legal purposes. I have already mentioned animal experimentation in the section on food additives, but there are other aspects of the problem which are relevant to a programme of individual change.

Tobacco is a 'cash' crop, which means that it is grown in the earth to provide money, not food or anything of real social value. So, on this basis alone, to smoke is to misuse the earth. But to smoke in a public place is to introduce carcinogenic (cancer forming) substances into the lungs and body of any non-smoker who is nearby. Thus the smoker could be seen as liable to prosecution by a non-smoker under the *Injurious Substances Act*. The charge would be attempted poisoning, and should such an action succeed, the result would be a ban on smoking in all public places.

The close relationship between inhalation of cigarette smoke and a number of serious diseases in man, including carcinoma of the lung, is one of the most impressive correlations in the history of medical research. This recognition has recently led to an examination of the effects on lung tissue of what are now termed 'new smoking materials', or NSM; and to this end, experiments on dogs have been performed.

A number of unanaesthetized beagle dogs were placed in restraining apparatus, and forced to inhale smoke, either from cigarettes or from new smoking material. Some of the dogs were treated in this way for a period of up to three years.

The alleged purpose of the experiments was to show whether new smoking material would be safer for humans to inhale than smoke from cigarettes made from tobacco.

Research on the effect of smoke on the linings of the lungs reveals that whatever type of smoke is inhaled, some inflammatory reaction is inevitable. In other words, there is no known smoke which can be inhaled without some pathological response in the lung tissues. Perhaps even more to the point, should experiments on dogs eventually reveal that the new smoking material is less harmful than tobacco, it would still be impossible for the experimenters to assert that it was harmless. Therefore, no data whatever could emerge from the experiments that would show that a human smoker with an average twenty to thirty years' smoking exposure would be less likely to suffer either from cancer of the lung, or from any of the other diseases to which cigarette smoking has already been linked. The experiments could never – however many dogs are treated in this way – produce sufficient evidence to support the safe exposure of humans to new smoking material.

It is thus true to say that the experiments are without any scientific value.

A basic clause of the Cruelty to Animals Act of 1876, upon

which the Home Office licence for animal experimentation depends, 'prohibits absolutely any experiment performed for the purpose of attaining manual skill or for purposes other than the advancement or new discovery of physiological knowledge or knowledge which will be useful for prolonging life or alleviating suffering'.

The experiments reported above cannot produce a new discovery, since the effect of smoke on the lungs is already well known. The knowledge is not physiological since it can never lead to a further understanding of the natural function of body systems. It is also doubtful that the experiments produce information which will prolong life or alleviate suffering, since they have the crucial defect that they compare a three-year smoking experience in a dog to a twenty- or thirty-year experience in a human.

Here then are scientifically valueless experiments involving massive and long-term cruelty to animals, performed for no other purpose than to give manufacturers some specious legal protection. I would be very interested to see the Home Office scientists who signed the licences for these experiments come forward to explain how they were able to endorse experiments of no scientific value. Questions of cruelty to animals are often vexed and emotive, but it is difficult to avoid the conclusion here that the regular and forcible insufflation of smoke into the lungs of a restrained and unanaesthetized dog is inconsistent with the wellbeing of the animal.

To smoke therefore is to misuse an area of the earth's surface, to cause suffering to animals and to shorten the life-span of non-smokers.

Many other substances which are part of everyday life are tested by experiments on animals. I have already suggested that oil-based detergents are unnecessary and that soap and water are equally efficient as cleaning agents. An additional reason for rejecting entropy-producing detergents is that fossil-fuel-based hair shampoos are still tested for irritant effect by dropping them undiluted into the eyes of unanaesthetized animals. In some cases, the damage to the coverings of eye and lids is both severe and long-lasting. It is obvious that strong detergents do irritate and damage the eye, and people can therefore learn not to put them in their eyes. So this test is not carried out to test the safety of the product, but to minimize the effect of any legal claim against manufacturers for damages. One experimenter dropping detergents into eyes of animals remarks: 'In this laboratory we classify as persistent all reactions that continue for twenty-one days after treatment.'[2] Treatment?

Cosmetics were once a simple mixture of oils, scents and pigments. Now lipstick may contain more than twenty separate ingredients. It is no more fit for function than the simpler variety: both colour the lips equally well. But many, if not all of the modern ingredients have been tested on animals often using the crude, brutalized and largely outdated method of testing I have already described, called the LD50 test, whereby batches of animals are given progressively larger doses of the substance under test until 50 per cent of the animals are killed.

There is no need at all to use cosmetics which have been tested in this way; an entire range of products called 'Beauty without Cruelty' is available in Great Britain, the constituents of which are guaranteed not to have been tested on animals. It has been objected that these cost more than ordinary cosmetics. They do, but people pay £9.25 for a bottle of aftershave, the contents of which cost slightly less than nine pence, so cost cannot be the central problem.

Perhaps the most selfish misuse of animals is to take them from their natural habitat to be confined in some urban animal ghetto for the entertainment of the public. The cruel and degrading sight of a cheetah, which normally cruises the savannah at 50 miles per hour, confined to a cage no bigger than an average living-room can be seen at any time amid the clanging alienated misery of the Regent's Park Zoo in London. Here also one can see elephants imprisoned in plain, concrete block houses and lions pacing in a crazed repetitive desperation over the brick and concrete floors of their prison cells.

Conversely, there are many naturalists with a deep-seated love for animals who have created conditions for animals which are better than those of their natural habitat, and who have bred or developed species which would normally have become extinct. The Gaian can thus make a stand not only by ceasing to support

---

[2] Burton, A. B. G. 1972. *Journal of Food Cosmetics Toxicology* 10. 209–17.

the urban ghetto zoos, but by making a point of enjoying the animals in the open zoos.

One of the few places where animals are cared for under conditions of social equality is the Woolly Monkey Colony near Looe in Cornwall. The colony consists of a house and grounds divided into two halves, one for the humans and the other for the monkeys. No attempt at all is made to force the monkeys into a subservient or secondary relationship, and human visitors are taught to wait patiently until the animals 'decide to be seen'. The last time I went to the colony, one visitor was determined, in spite of advice, to maintain his position of dominance. We were all sitting playing with the monkeys, who were climbing up and down chairs and tables and generally enjoying themselves. This man began to jeer and banter at them, and his behaviour finally went so far against the feelings of the others present that an embarrassed silence developed. Then a monkey he was jeering at climbed on a table, picked up a bowl of peeled and chopped fruit, sidled up to the man and emptied the bowl all over his suit. I swear the monkey winked at the rest of us afterwards. To visit the colony is to learn more about communication with animals in an hour than in a lifetime of academic zoological training.

Animals can give us back the very breath of living. They are life, they have knowledge and wisdom in as much profusion as we have, and we can listen to them if we wish. In their natural habitat they are part of Gaia, their knowledge is ancient and accurate and by necessity related to the real arts of survival. They have no sentiment, only need. But they do have the ability to relate to us if we look for the signs and signals of their language. Not only do they have a minutely varied alphabet of sound and body language, but also, I suspect, they can communicate among themselves in a way akin to what we, in human terms, call telepathy. I believe that we can learn to be sensitive to their communications in much the same way.

Our future survival depends on our ability to recover community with animals.

But what about the rights of the cabbage? If occupancy and existence are the basis for rights, then vegetables have rights;

and if we do not eat meat then we have either to kill vegetables or starve. So we eat living things and offend those rights. Here again we can only compromise and eat the minimum commensurate with health, and thus learn to *tread more lightly upon the earth*.

We need to be more fully exposed to the damage we cause. Much of present-day life shuts away the darker aspects of the comforts we take for granted. A single visit to a slaughterhouse would, I am sure, convince many people that meat eating is impossible. The clean symmetrical pattern of holes in the wall belies the fumes and entropy of the power station supplying the electricity, just as the carefully shaped lamb chop in the plastic package belies the terror and suffering of the animals waiting on the death-line.

It is often said that there is one basic distinction between plants and animals: that plants do not possess senses, nervous system or brain. So conventional biologists and botanists assert that plants cannot feel or suffer. But now an entirely new and extraordinary school of thought has emerged which suggests that plants do have some sensory or feeling equivalent.[3]

Communication between man and man is obvious when it is language, and less obvious when it is extra-sensory. It is enormously more controversial when it is claimed that there can be communication between man and plant. At first sight the idea that plants have any equivalent of senses is absurd, and yet there are descriptions of truly unusual events in this area. In one experiment, for example, electrical signals were recorded from the leaf of a plant and then live shrimps were dropped into boiling water in an adjoining room. Each time the plant 'responded' to the death of a shrimp by a burst of electrical activity. Or did it? Others have tried to repeat this experiment and failed. I am personally doubtful about the protocol behind much of this research, but it is an area of potential growth.

It is easy to lapse into absurdity. Are we really going to go about life not even treading on the grass because it might suffer? No, but we *can* tread more lightly: once more, take from the

---

[3] *The Secret Life of Plants*. Peter Tompkins, Christopher Bird. Penguin Books, London 1975.

earth only what is absolutely necessary and be continually conscious of what we take.

I recently met an Indian Swami and told him some of the thoughts I have expressed in this book. He listened very patiently and then smiled. He told me that the absolute basis of his life-long training had been to develop his relationship with what I have called Gaia, or the earth organism. Each morning he begins his day by talking to the living earth and asking its permission to put his feet on its chest. I was with him for about seven days on an almost deserted island in the Indian Ocean and throughout that time he consumed only fruit, vegetables and milk. He is aged seventy-six and looks about fifty.

We can begin to find a different basis for living if we admit the possibility of a creative relationship between plant and human. The Findhorn community in the north of Scotland, for example, has achieved an astonishing growth of plants in an unfertile area by creating such a relationship. There is sharp controversy about Findhorn, and some say that their results are flukes. But the people of Findhorn see themselves as having a firm religious basis for their way of life and they are, in their own way, finding their connection with the earth organism.

I began this second part of the book by declaring some principles of Gaian living:

1. To develop a minimum entropy way of life.
2. To move consumption as high up the solar drive chain as possible.
3. To re-create a dependence on the solar drive chain, and to reject the use of fossil fuels as far as possible.
4. To restore the interrelationship between ourselves and the earth organism and to reject any ideologies which propose dominance over it.
5. To evolve a new science which has as its basic premise: that we are an integral part of a single earth organism.

For reasons of space I have confined suggestions for change to the basic needs of ordinary living. Now seems the time to summarize the lifestyle of an emergent Gaian:

A Gaian is a person who rejects ideas of self-sufficiency in isolation and rejects both the capitalist and communist analyses of society, since both ideologies are equally responsible for unnecessary damage to the earth organism via the processes of the centralized industrial society.

A Gaian is also a person who holds that the human race is an integral part of a single life-form, sometimes called the earth organism, the earth spirit or Gaia; and that no sustainable future for mankind can be achieved until a decision is made to put human needs second to the requirements of that life-form.

A Gaian is also a non-violent revolutionary who holds that the greater part of the industrial process will have to be abandoned to minimize personal entropy debt, and also to help bring about a transformation in society which broadens the idea of personal entropy reduction into a more strategic policy of planetary care and mutual symbiosis with the earth organism.

A Gaian is someone who has decided to eat food which has been grown as high up the solar drive chain as is possible, and who rejects nearly all products of the high technological food process: a person who will not consume artificial colourings, flavourings or additives of no nutritional function, and who rejects meat and all packaging.

A Gaian will not consume instant coffee or instant anything, does not use a deep-freeze and cooks on the most functional and decoration-free cookers or in a hay-box.

He or she washes in a shower and not a bath, does not use a washing machine, and wears simple clothes made of natural fibre which do not need ironing.

Gaians live in shelters which are made of materials which incur a low entropy debt and which can be tooled using basic machines only.

Gaians do as little work for money outside the boundary of their dwelling as is practicable, and instead spend much of their waking day working inside their own entropy boundary to make what they need from more basic materials.

The Gaian approach to health rejects the products of high technological medicine as far as possible, and in particular rejects antibiotics and many other drugs except where to do so puts life directly at risk. A Gaian also holds that the process of health has largely been expropriated by industrial medicine and its proponents, and demands instead that many of the skills and useful practices of medicine be made available to lay people as a basic right.

He or she also rejects all non-functional and decorative machinery, does not celebrate Christmas with a tree and does not use any product or substance which has been tested on animals or which has been produced by animals under unnatural conditions.

A Gaian sounds very much like a priggish bore leading a grey restricted life and who moralizes at all his friends if they look like enjoying themselves.

So where is the fun of it?

I have discovered *exactly* where it is. It is finding out that there are real and creative ways of coping, alternative to the ready-made solutions offered by the industrial machine.

It is to do with my joy on the day my first solar panel actually *gave* me hot water free of all charge, with my delight at the moment when a small bulb on the end of my fourth or fifth wind generator actually lit up without using centrally made power and without exchanging money; and with my horror when I looked in at the window of a butcher's shop and saw a post-mortem room.

It is to do with the reappropriation of skills and the absolutely delicious sense of freedom the discovery brings; and it is to do with the re-creation of confidence in the body and its self-repair mechanisms.

The fun also comes from the knowledge that choice reappears in direct proportion to the relearning of self-supporting skills, and that the choice gives freedom to be responsible. It is also, blessedly, to do with the rejection of authority and the ability to be self-maintaining to a greater degree than before.

It is also to do with the lovely, heady confidence which returns when the ugly and despoliating products of the industrial machine can be genuinely rejected from the centre of the being.

And finally it is to do with the clearing of the senses. The world begins to look different. It looks more rounded, it smells sweeter and it swells with life.

The fun and enjoyment also come from the knowledge that

possessions need not necessarily involve damage to Gaia and that beauty, comfort, warmth and shelter can all be attained without dead rivers, poisoned land and foul air.

Right at the beginning I claimed that the changes I have proposed can lead to the re-establishment of an almost lost sense of vision which was once as natural to us as the ability to see with our eyes. In this next and final section I want to try to justify that claim.

PART THREE
An Age of Gaia

26

A Post-Industrial Revolution

In a high technology environment, we spend a very large proportion of our waking time dealing with external technical activities. Attention is increasingly directed outwards towards the management of a tool or a system. We *dial* the telephone, *plug in* the electric kettle, *switch on* the central heating, *drive* the car, *push buttons* on a calculator, *fill in* machine-printed forms, *press more buttons* on the television set, *programme* an electronic watch, *select* a grade of petrol on the pump and *set controls* on the cooker. All these tools for living were originally sold to us on the understanding that they would ease life and make it more comfortable. And it is obvious that many of them do. It *is* far easier to telephone a friend than to write a letter and a calculator *is* much quicker at doing arithmetic than the brain. But I suggest that this apparent ease and convenience has been at the expense of an inner sensitivity; that in spending so much time in accelerating the pace of life by the use of these tools, our ability to see beyond the limits of technical practicalities has been hampered. We no longer have enough time, or even perhaps so strong a wish, to contemplate an inner life; or indeed any relationship which may exist between inner life and the elements of nature outside the boundary of our living space. In the preceding sections I have suggested individual changes which can reduce dependence on the industrial society and which reduce personal entropy debt, but now I am going to look at these changes as a means of extension of the senses and the development of a more rewarding view of things.

Control of natural systems has become an integral way of life on a national and international scale. And so, in microcosm, we are encouraged by the toymakers to believe that to control machines for ourselves is also an important part of living. The machines that we operate are all part of a carefully designed and maintained illusion that their use allows us to be free and separate from any other consideration. But I suggest that what they really achieve is a suppression of sensitivities and a loss of skills.

Because we assume that human affairs are the only proper concern of humans, we put the rest of the physical and living world into a secondary position. Our concepts and ideas are full of references to 'superior' and 'inferior', as if to suggest that because we have acquired language, self-awareness, reason and the tools which are a product of these qualities, we are entitled to assume a general position of dominance and control. Of course we do dominate and control, our toolmaking technology is highly effective. But we have made the error of assuming that because pragmatic technology works so well, our science works just as well also. Yet it is *science*, our body of systematic and formalized knowledge about nature, which has gone so hopelessly wrong.

Apollo was a superb tool, a tool to put man on the moon. But no new *scientific* knowledge was necessary to make it work. It was the result of a decision by an affluent military-industrial state to assemble large numbers of talented toolmakers. Following that decision, a landing on the moon was a near certainty. The necessary knowledge of metallurgy, ballistics, rocketry and space physiology was either already in existence or to be had for the hiring. It was not 'one great step for man', it was just the apotheosis of a race of talented toolmakers.

Current institutional science teaches that it is *science* that leads to control, without realizing that it is *toolmaking* and *technology* which does so, and not science. It is a nuclear *tool* which can gouge whole islands out of the earth's surface and it is a *tool* called an aeroplane which carries people across continents. These tools are clearly science-based: mathematics, physics and chemistry give powerful and consistent control over materials. But because they can be seen to work in this way, we are encouraged to assume that they are the proper basis for the understanding of the universe and the natural world. The truth is that the sciences are only consistent within their own limits.

This fundamental error is now built into the policy of nearly all countries which have developed a science and a high technology. It spread, again by consensus between governments and toymakers, because of ordinary competition between nation-states in the joint names of economic growth and defence.

An exploitative and aggressively despoliating science is operated at a maximum rate until such time as an acceptable rate of economic growth has been assured and a nation-state is seen to be a success; but the technologies which follow this premise rarely have the interests of people or Gaia at heart. Moreover the projected growth is never achieved, and so the aggressive technology has to continue in permanent pursuit of an unattainable goal. Aggressive, toymaking science also suits the needs of military industrial states excellently. The weapon-toymakers are perennially ingenious, and to gain carte-blanche for their murderous designs, they still proclaim that their standards are value-free and that knowledge is somehow precious and pure and never to be tampered with by ideologies. Yet from the 'Marxist potato' of Lysenko to the 'political electrons' of the failed thermodynamic generator 'Zeta', science has always been heavily subject to external political and social stress, and is tampered with daily.

But the tools we control *do* still work, Concorde still flies, nuclear power stations function and next year's car appears more or less on time.

Man has walked erect for more than two million years, in relation to which period our present machine society has lasted a mere instant. Yet already we are moving into a stage which will almost certainly end in a 'post-industrial revolution'. The basis of current industrial activity is now largely irrational and has no basis in terms of human need, or common sense.

Consider a nuclear power station, for example. If, instead of analysing the station using money as a basis, we look at its efficiency in terms of 'energy accountancy', a very different picture emerges. On the debit side goes the fabrication energy in its construction: the mining, refining and constructional energy used in the steel pressure sphere, the buildings, turbines and heat exchangers. Then, on the energy credit side, goes the electricity that the station starts to produce. More than one estimate has now shown that only in about the fifteenth year of operation does the station show a net production of energy and when we discover that the station has a total operating life of only twenty years, we find that it can only actually produce net energy for five. Finally, yet more energy has to be expended to de-commission the station, and this has again to be added to the debit side. It looks now as though some nuclear power stations may produce a net energy loss and anything more insane would be very hard to imagine. This calculation is quite apart from the enormous dangers to all life-forms that nuclear technology represents, and the tremendous entropic and pollution debt incurred by its operation. The nuclear power station has no real function other than as a cathedral in which to celebrate myths. Cathedral designers are even engaged to design the building.[1]

Bear in mind that these generators are being built in the UK, where there is already a surplus of electricity generating equipment.

By the same token, an oil- or coal-fired power station converts only about 28 per cent of the energy in its fuel into electricity, the remaining 72 per cent being released as low-grade warmth or entropy which can never again be used to do work. Since a power station produces more heat than electricity, I have renamed it a 'waste heat generating station'.

We know in our heart of hearts that there is no rational basis at all for these destructive technologies. So how do we come to agree to participate, however uneasily, in a society which disorders the planet on this massive and unsustainable scale? How is it that we can agree to invest millions of pounds in industries which produce artefacts of no practical function, and which incur a net loss in energy and enormous amounts of entropy? Where was the initial mistake?

The industrial revolution had one great consequence relevant to our argument. For the first time animal and human muscle power, and the natural power systems of wind and water, could be replaced by the prime mover or engine. Up until that time, fuel had been used only to produce heat and not work, and so in one expansive vision, industrial man saw a final release from toil: *the engine would provide*.

[1] Sir Basil Spence designed both Coventry Cathedral and the main building of Dungeness B nuclear power station.

But once engines became commonplace, whole landscapes were systematically ravaged to provide the necessary wood and coal fuel. In the Swansea Valley, for example, there is a detailed recorded history of despoliation on a massive scale. Whole forests were destroyed in a few years: the air was continually black with smoke, and towns glowed crimson at night from the fire of the steel mills. In 1874 the poet Gordon Bottomley vividly portrayed the terrible scene.

To Iron-Founders and Others

When you destroy a blade of grass
You poison England at her roots;
Remember no man's food can pass
Where evermore no green life shoots.

You force the birds to wing too high
Where your unnatural vapours creep;
Surely the living rocks shall die
When birds no rightful distance keep.

You have brought down the firmament
And yet no heaven is more near;
You shape huge needs without event
And half-made men believe and fear.

Your worship is your furnaces,
Which, like old idols, lost obscenes,
Have molten bowels; your vision is
Machines for making more machines.

O, you are busied in the night,
Preparing destinies of rust,
Iron misused must turn to blight
And dwindle to a tetter'd crust.

The grass, forerunner of life, has gone
But plants that spring in ruins and shards
Attend until your dream is done:
I have seen hemlock in your yards.

The generations of the worm
Know not your loads piled on their soil;
Their knotted ganglions shall wax firm
Till your strong flagstones heave and toil.

When the old hollow'd earth is crack'd,
And when, to grasp more power and feasts,
Its ores are emptied, wasted, lack'd,
The middens of your burning beasts

> Shall be raked over till they yield
> Last priceless slags for fashionings high,
> Ploughs to wake grass in every field,
> Chisels men's hands to magnify.

The engine was a tremendous boost to the self-confidence of the engineer, who was encouraged to experiment with increasingly complicated machines. And here is one of the most important beginnings of our present technological hubris. *Complexity* and *size* became equated with *efficiency* and *success*. An iron-based myth of dominance, power and control took hold, and the technologist became a hero emulated and encouraged by the population at large.

As the machines evolved and the 'manufactory' or workshop grew into the 'factory' there was another important development. Prior to the industrial revolution, technology had been confined to small workshops where some degree of control was maintained by the craftsmen doing the work. But as machines grew more capable, the factories became larger and more densely populated and so control of technology passed into the hands of factory owners and managers. The theorist and the specialist also appeared, and so *mystification* began. Each industrial process was judged in economic terms only, and not related to the quality of life. As long as an artefact sold, its production was assured.

The industrial revolution was certainly the beginning, but we cannot get away guilt-free by blaming dead engineers. Once the history of our present age is written – probably by aliens or intelligent micro-chips – it is the economists who will emerge as the primary deceivers. They will be judged for assessing human activity in terms of profit and loss alone, and for attempting to justify greed with empty assertions about raising the standard of living. It is not the standard of life we need to be concerned about, but the quality of life with Gaia.

We now have, as a direct descendant of the industrial revolution, a massive, centralized industrial society managed by an entirely undemocratic body of relatively unskilled people, who control situations they are not equipped to understand, and who can maintain control only by a deliberate process of public mystification. The phrases 'leave it to the experts', 'it is a highly

technical matter' and 'calculations show' are all used as mysti-
fying and protective clichés by the toymakers and the managers
to prevent proper access by the public to their work. Experts
produced technical calculations, which showed the need for a
third London Airport – except that the calculations were wrong
and there was no such need.

The only purpose of jargon is to mystify, and to make the
toymaker appear privy to esoteric knowledge. There was never
anything difficult about either science or technology. Any difficulty arises entirely from voluntary or involuntary inarticulacy.
All of science can easily be explained, using words to be found
in *The Oxford English Dictionary*. If a scientist denies this simple
truth, he has something to hide. Obscurantism prevents accountability, encourages respect and keeps a salary coming in.

As long as high technology is accepted as having passed
beyond the control of ordinary people, none of the necessary
changes for an age of Gaia will occur and the toymakers will
continue controlling and wrecking the planet, without reference
either to people or to Gaia. Neither, as we have seen, is there a
realistic basis for change in any political ideology.

But there are rapidly increasing numbers of people who have
already realized intuitively that their future is not all assured,
and that the influence of the toymakers is lethal both to
themselves and the earth organism; people who have decided to
protect themselves against the lies and blandishments of the
marketplace and the expropriation of skills and freedoms by the
state; people who instead want to evolve simpler ways of getting
food, warmth, shelter and health. This dispersed and unorgan-
ized band of stalwarts offers the one great hope for a survivable
future, and I dedicate this book to them with love and respect.
At present they are frequently demeaned with labels such as
'drop out', 'eco freak', 'middle-class élitist' and 'radical'. These
are titles bestowed by an increasingly nervous establishment – I
have been called all these and many more besides.

To abandon some of the expensive and entropic machines
which now clutter our living space is a first move in clearing the
senses. It is not only a move towards a reduction of personal
entropy debt: it also clears the way for the relearning of survival
skills which are more directly related to the pace of nature than

the artificially accelerated pace which the use of the machines has generated. By adopting this mental set, the industrial age can be clearly seen for what it really is: a massive barrier in the path of human evolution.

Perhaps it was inevitable that the whole grinding, despoliating Behemoth be allowed its head until the absolute necessity for a post-industrial age – an age of Gaia – was obvious to all.

But something sinister and dangerous has now begun to evolve which will make any move towards a post-industrial revolution and an age of Gaia more difficult than the mere recognition of the problem. Centralized control of technology has now evolved to a point where it is no longer in the control even of its controllers and their appointed toymakers: it is developing a life of its own.

27

The Cybernarchy

There is a fundamental conflict between the freedom of the individual and the authority of the state which has never been resolved. Rousseau[1] described its nature very clearly: '. . . whether there can be a form of association which will defend and protect, with the whole common force, the person and property of each associate, and by which every person, while uniting himself with all, shall obey only himself and remain as free as before'.

Political leaders still assert that 'democracy' must be protected to prevent 'anarchy'. But the 'democracy' they refer to is now no more than a carefully maintained myth, to encourage the mistaken belief that the possession of the vote offers a real chance to influence matters of state. Nothing could be further from the truth. The word 'anarchy' is used, in contrast, as a universal term of abuse to describe *any* action which would affect the stability of the state in *any* way.

Freedom of choice and autonomy automatically create responsibility, and I have suggested already that this responsibility can no longer be directed at human affairs alone if we are to survive, but must be directed first of all towards the needs and demands of Gaia.

Democracy has been said to be a natural extension of autonomy towards a generally agreed collective action; implying that people can, by consensus, give laws to themselves and so agree to a measure of self-control. But in current industrial societies nothing of the sort obtains. In Europe and the United States, democracy is evolving into a fully automated state which is

[1] Jean Jacques Rousseau. *The Social Contract*. Book Four.

wholly autocratic, and shows real signs of becoming an intelligently directed mega-individual. *Homo sapiens* may be giving way
to a new species: the intelligent micro-chip.

Democracy may take any of three main forms: unanimous
direct, representational or majoritarian. Unanimous direct
democracy allows the whole of the population to vote on every
issue and so each enacted law is the wish of the people and
Rousseau's dilemma is resolved. Autonomy and authority can
co-exist. Unfortunately, a single vote against any motion defeats
the motion, so in a population of 49 million people there is no
possibility at all of total consensus. Moreover, direct democracy
would be impossible to operate in a centralized society unless all
members of the populace possessed an electronic device such as
an 'Instant plebiscite button', by which they could make their
views known on every issue.

Direct democracy can function best in a small community
with a pre-existent and powerful common resolve – such perhaps
as an Israeli kibbutz. And it may be that in a Gaian community
there would be a similar driving ethic to maintain a continuing
basis for the lifestyle of the community.

Many communes in Britain begin with great enthusiasm, go
through a period of great success and stability, and then develop
factions; finally losing impetus and dispersing. I think that this
often happens partly because the communards become increasingly aware of the partial parasitism such an attempted act of
self-sufficiency implies, and partly because they see the enterprise as a means towards internal personal development only; a
search after Karma, or even perhaps another set of human-
centred rules. So once the commune is working and a degree of
self-sufficiency and separation from high technological society
has been achieved, motivation to continue seems often to dwindle
and disappear. Again, this is not to make a fundamental criticism
of the communes – they are the most effective basis for a counter-
action to the centralized machine society. But they do often seem
to lack external reference and motivation. Kibbutzim, on the
other hand, know very well that they are constantly in danger
and this maintains concentration and drive at a high level.

The development of a Gaian commune, on the other hand,
would begin from extra-human reference points: living as high

up the solar drive chain as possible and with a minimum of entropy production. So there would be a constantly present drive towards evolution and a constant reminder that survival is not possible without continually adjusting life to the demands of the dynamic of the earth organism.

The classical answers to the problems of direct democracy are either representative or majoritarian. A representative method, again, can work in a small group, but in centralized societies the system varies between the delegation to a single agent of the right to vote, and a complete abrogation of the decision-making function of the voter. The problem stems from the sheer number of issues to be represented. A parliamentary candidate, for example, may be presented with three principal issues in his ward. On the first he may have to consider two possible lobbies, on the second four and on the third three. So he has to appear in Parliament representing twenty-four different possibilities, for discussion by a government which will probably allocate him a total of ten minutes' time each year to present them. A democratically elected MP therefore ceases altogether to be the proper political agent of his voters, and instead becomes an unwitting commissioner for the existing system. The people who elected him have lost effective representation. Rousseau made the point with some anger.

> The people of England deceive themselves when they fancy they are free; they are so in fact only during the election of members of parliament; for, as soon as a new one is elected, they are again in chains and are nothing. And thus by the use they make of their brief moments of liberty, they deserve to lose it.[2]

Decision making on European technology has been entirely removed from individual people, who have therefore lost the chance of enacting any laws of self-control and thus cannot exercise the responsibility which could follow choice. The first and most important quality of humanity has been once again expropriated by the state. Management of the planet is now increasingly in the hands of the toymakers and the bureaucrats.

[2] J. J. Rousseau. *The Social Contract*. Book Three.

Majoritarian democracy – each man one vote and the majority deciding – thus seems on the face of it to be the only fair and practical way of decision making. But it is again extremely doubtful whether any personal autonomy can be preserved under its aegis. The majority in favour of an enacted law are unanimous and are therefore fairly bound by the law; but the minority may be equally against that law. If, on the one hand, a dissenting citizen reserves the right to deny co-operation with the state, he or she is denying it automatic authority and so can preserve autonomy. If, on the other hand, the citizen decides to submit to the authority of the majority-elected state and agrees to abide by its laws, he loses autonomy. In practice, a simple majority rule fails to work in the terms of Rousseau's dilemma, again because in a densely populated centralized society, the crude mathematical power of the majority may suppress a very large number of wishes both for change and for reacquisition of responsibility.

If the capacity for responsibility is expropriated by a non-representative state, then it follows that violent revolution must take place, since there is no other way of changing the situation. There are already anti-nuclear riots in France and Germany, and if this lethally dangerous technology continues to be forced on people without their approval, these must inevitably spread. They represent, in part, a bitter anger directed against expropriation of choice by the state.

Since, as we have found, under the existing system of centralized high technology, direct democracy is impracticable, and representative and majoritarian democracies provide neither autonomy, real decision-making capability nor responsibility for the individual, what is it in the system, since it does still seem to work, that keeps things so effectively under control?

In Western Europe, any semblance of democracy is now largely replaced by an executive bureaucracy whose principal task is to achieve agreement with the toymakers, and to maintain control by secret decisions and by progressive deskilling of the citizen. The means of obtaining food, warmth, shelter and health have all been systematically expropriated by the executive, and as a direct consequence, choice and responsibility have also been removed. All that is offered in return to the citizen is the totally dishonest illusion of an effective vote.

The voter is offered the choice between what are still termed the 'left' and the 'right', although all that is really offered is a choice between different puppet-managers of the same executive industrial machine.

On the face of it, of course, we have a bewildering range of choice. We can choose from enormous varieties of clothes and food, we can choose what film or television programme we would like to watch, and we can choose which package tour to take to a country of our choice. We can choose which doctor, solicitor or plumber to advise us and our religion, at least in the West. But without the acts of change which I have suggested to separate the individual from the entropic society, no real choice of lifestyle is possible. There is no viable, alternative urban alternative to the electricity offered by the Central Waste Heat Generating Board, there is little or no choice in housing; draconian planning laws and antique and restrictive building regulations limit choice between derisory limits. And there is little or no choice for a person of average income in the way he or she maintains health. In many of the essential parts of life we are forced to take part in the destructive processes of the industrial Behemoth, and are deprived of any chance to behave in a responsible way towards the earth.

With few exceptions, the executives of government are almost as powerless to change the leviathan as the voters. A minister of either party may be expected to take on the management of a staff of 10,000 at two days' notice, and leave for another similar post two months later having seen on average 2 per cent of the output from the ministry. Meanwhile the multiple brains and operational systems of the essentially cybernetic organization he is supposed to lead continue to function normally without even a pause. A minister recently told me: 'I feel like a perpetual new boy who is kept from changing anything by continuous overwork given to me by people I have never met.'

At the next level of organization, the system is maintained by a protective consensus among bureaucrats, first because they are nervous of the incomprehensible complexity of the system they are asked to work, second because they will do nothing exceptional for fear of losing their job, and third, because they are anxious about public opinion. And since they are anxious about public opinion they create a web of mystification to prevent the public understanding what they are doing. Obscurantism and secrecy prevent accountability, and keep the computers running.

The earliest computers were no more than sophisticated arithmetical machines, but computers have now evolved that can learn by experience, ask questions, control people, hold elementary conversations and write poetry. Computer power and complexity has increased tenfold in the last twenty years or so. We have had maybe four or five generations of machines, and already they seem to be evolving in a semi-Darwinian manner – the fittest being those that are sold most often. But now a strategic development of an extremely serious nature has appeared: men and computers in dialogue are planning the next generations of computer. Men and computers have implants in each other's brains in every sense except for the actual surgery, so that the whole of man's global experience and intuition has become linked with machines whose reasoning power is hundreds of millions of times more rapid and error-free than his own.

We are no longer limited by the size of our skull; our brain may now cover an office block!

The significant point is that, as this psycho-mechanical creature evolves, man the designer is steadily abrogating his tasks to the machine. As the machine learns, machine talks to machine and machine teaches machine. The conversations between almost uncountable hordes of micro-processors cut clear across national boundaries, political strategies and the privacy of the individual.

So we now have an emergent robot state, which I have called the cybernarchy. It is as if a new mega-individual has evolved somewhere in the gap between political leaders and people, and it is pursuing a course of self-perpetuation regardless of any other consideration. This mega-individual is a feltwork of flesh and micro-chips, looking after itself at the expense of people.

The great naturalist Eugene Marais[3] considered the ant colony to be a single organized individual. By analogy, the nation state, or now the continent state, behaves increasingly like a self-organizing and self-managing individual made of hardware and software: machines and people.

The robot state, the cybernarchy, is a complete antithesis to the concept of the state expressed by Hegel, who saw it as a supra-organism, but one which embodied archetypal moral values: 'The state is the actually existing realized moral life' . . . 'truth is the unity of the universal and subjective Will and the universal is to be found in the state, in its laws, its universal and rational arrangements. The State is the Divine Idea as it exists on earth.'[4]

Hegel's attempted deification of the state led to a hollow attempt to justify war, on the basis that the whole duty of the individual is to support the independence and sovereignty of the state. He thought that war for this reason . . . 'has the highest significance, that through it the moral health of the people is preserved . . .'

In contrast, the modern high-technological state is fast becoming an entity, an electronic-protoplasmic individual of variable external form, but with no built-in Hegelian morality. This entity has one overriding goal: self-maintenance and self-perpetuation. And it possesses one great advantage over ordinary humanity: its rate of activity is quite outside any real human management or understanding – a point recently explored by Alvin Toffler.[5] The cybernarchy can extract, store, alter and transmit information in microseconds. Information about decisions can flash around global networks at a speed which no human perception can possibly grasp. And since each machine decision was programmed by a specialist in that decision, it follows also that others within the state organism cannot follow out the details of another specialist's action and so validate or invalidate the decision, since they do not know the other's techniques in full detail. The blind lead the blind.

There are no generalists within the state system because of the

[3] Eugene Marais: *The Soul of the White Ant.*
[4] Georg Wilhelm Hegel. *The Philosophy of History.*
[5] Alvin Toffler. *The Ecospasm Report.* Bantam Books, New York 1975.

impossible amount of knowledge to be absorbed, and so there can be no one who understands how all of it works. Yet, at present, the embryonic cybernarchy is wholly dependent on human operation, and if its human operators were suddenly to extricate themselves, it would collapse. But it is worthwhile recalling that the basic logic and design for a self-replicating robot was first published in 1944 by mathematician J. Van Neumann. If the compulsive skills of the toymakers continue to improve, Van Neumann's machine may evolve into a different mode of activity and finally declare people redundant.

And this, curiously, is a relatively optimistic view of the changes to come because, for perhaps the first time in our history, we do not have to declare one class of humans to be ideologically guilty. It is not going to be a necessary theatrical event to submit a group of people to contrived political trials as ritual exorcism. Neither, conversely, will there be any revolutionary heroes to idolize. Instead, it is the rapidly evolving cybernarch which has to be opposed and dismantled: not because it holds the wrong set of beliefs and not because it is oppressing one section of the populace unfairly, but because it is evolving in its own right as a self-stabilizing entity. But unlike its human or animal equivalent it has the capacity, using the progressively efficient means of communication built into it by no one but ourselves, to evolve and spread beyond human boundaries.

Nobody caused the state to happen except man, and so it may be that one of our real roles was not the self-appointed *Homo sapiens* – what an extraordinary arrogance this title implies – but instead to be a tool evolved by an unknown process to design and build an experimental life-form. *We may not be man the toolmaker, but man the tool.*

If we can clearly see that our 'human' properties are leaking away into an evolving supra-state entity, then we can also begin to disassemble the creature before it reduces us to the level of cells in its body. If we do not recognize this possibility, it may be that like Mumford's 'mega-machine',[6] our work as tools is almost complete, and once the self-perpetuating global state-entity is fully operational we shall be dispensed with and

[6] Lewis Mumford. *The Myth of the Machine.* Vols 1 and 2, Secker & Warburg, London 1967.

relegated to the position of drones in the body of the cybernarch, bereft of power, reason or self-awareness: pink protoplasmic appendages to an intelligent entity covering a planet.

Throughout nature there are examples of this drive towards organization of 'individual' systems. The ant colony and the beehive are both variants of societies wherein the individual is wholly programmed, perhaps, as Marais believed, for a particular role in the mega-individual. At a much simpler level in the earth organism, the mould *Dyctostelium* has the strange capacity to gather individual mobile cells together in one place and to create a single mobile individual, which then breaks up again into small individual units when the larger body has reached another site.

But we *do* still have choice of action, a quality which neither ant, bee nor mould appears to have, and so we can choose to allow our individualities to be diluted out of existence into the global cybernarch or to evolve into a form which is directly and primarily related to the earth organism from which we sprang.

Why do this? Why not just enjoy the fruits of high technology for as many generations as possible, until finally, with a faint murmur of apology to no one in particular, and replete with gratifications, we pupate into our final role of moron servants to a non-human but stable planetary entity?

Why do I keep emphasizing the need for a changed way of life related to the earth organism? Why not just get into our chromium-plated life-pods, close the hatch, switch on the multi-dimensional media and wait for the machine to stop?

Because we have already nearly lost an absolutely basic and vital *human* quality which we once had. Colin Wilson[7] calls this Factor X, and I too believe that we could once see much further and with different eyes than we can now; and that this expanded vision has been covered over, muted and almost destroyed by the development of the machine society. I believe also that this sense of expanded vision is the central hope for a real and lasting human happiness.

It was the development of the machine age by *itself*, with its

[7] *The Occult*. Colin Wilson. Hodder & Stoughton, 1971.

temporary promise of relief from toil and its concepts of domination and control, which was the primary fault. In one move, we changed allegiance from the natural world to the machine, and began to believe the illusion that we never again had to search for the means of survival among the flow and currents of the earth organism. We achieved 'progress' at the expense of sensitivity, and now stand at the pinnacle of technical achievement surrounded by giant glittering Golems of our own making, quite unable to see the perpetual richness of the earth organism or the extinction which automatically follows separation from it.

Our sense of reality has become tragically confined by the Wagnerian promise of high technology and our imaginations confined by the strait-jacket of reductionist analysis.

A tree to a proponent of the old science – properly called applied toymaking – is made of chlorophyl, phloem and xylem, and it works by transpiration and respiration, metaphors of mechanistic explanation. But to an emergent Gaian scientist, these preliminaries are only a framework to flesh out the whole description of the tree. Indeed in the first part of this book, I used concepts from the old science to outline the structure and function of the earth organism, but the descriptions were never intended as more than an initial statement. The statement is no more than to say that a poem is composed of words.

Science was once the province of those 'Natural Philosophers' to whom I have already paid tribute: people who, as an act of homage to the miraculous beauty of all that lay about them, sought to understand so that they could achieve a more rational basis for their delight in the natural world; people who fell in love with part of nature and sought to know more about it, not to dominate or to change by force.

Goethe was a poet, and also a highly original natural philosopher who saw plants and trees as highly individual life-forms. But even during his lifetime, his academic colleagues attacked his idea of the *metamorphosis of plants*, since he was a poet and therefore could not possibly understand the more pragmatic mystifications of the botanists and taxonomists. If Goethe were alive today he would still be ridiculed by the scientific institutions, because he saw nature in poetic metaphors and did not have a Ph.D. And yet his ideas of the nature of trees and plants expressed in *The Metamorphosis of Plants* were highly disciplined and one of the main starting points for the present-day classification of plants.

His ideas on colour also absolutely infuriated Newton. In what has become known as 'the most glamorous experiment in the world', Newton placed a prism in the path of a sunbeam and demonstrated the fan of colours which appeared. Newton claimed that the prism *revealed* the colours. Goethe disagreed fundamentally and said instead that the prism *manufactured* the colours – a profoundly different world view to which I shall return.

Behind the appearance and structure of a tree, Goethe saw more fundamental patterns of life. He believed that evolution was not, as Darwin saw it, a response to external influences, but a pressure from archetypal life-forms which gave rise to all the variegated structures to be seen in the natural world. He wrote of the '*Urorganismus*', the archetypal organism from which all the versatile structures of living creatures could develop, and the '*Urpflanze*', a non-material archetypal life-form which could develop into the great panoply of trees and plants, each changing its form according to environmental conditions.

He visualized the physical appearance of plants as a temporary image representing the driving force of the archetype. The drive was from the metaphysical to the physical. He derived great satisfaction from these concepts, and spoke repeatedly of his 'joy and ecstasy' in pursuing them. But when he first tried to publish an essay about them, he was crudely rebuffed both by friends and publishers. He commented wryly: 'The public demand that every man remain in his own field. Nowhere would anyone grant that science and poetry can be united.'

Goethe thought that a tree had just as full and real an existence while still in the form of a seed. The leaves, branches and trunk were already in existence and it was only the absence of warmth, moisture and earth which prevented the physical structure of the tree fleshing out into its spectral form. Nowadays a scientist would prefer to talk about Goethe's ghost tree as 'encoded' in DNA molecules in the seed, or the seed as containing a 'tape-recording' or a 'blueprint' for the tree in the form of genes and chromosomes – which is a good example of how the toymakers try to fit everything inside a technological metaphor. The terms 'tape-recording' and 'blueprint' evoke powerful images of artefacts from the machine society, and it is this kind of confidently hard-edged description which specifically prevents us from *seeing* a tree – and, which is so important to our re-evolution, seeing our relationship to the tree.

If to survive we have no choice but to go back to a strict dependence on the natural currents of the earth organism, then Goethe was the truer and more appropriate thinker for a Gaian science. The person who wrote of tape-recordings, blueprints and DNA was an ambitious mechanic trying to reduce something too big for him to understand into terms of physical hardware.

It may be that poets are the most appropriate scientists for the difficult future we face, and that the people who now call themselves scientists are *savants manquées*, with nothing further to contribute except mechanistic descriptions which prevent our eyes opening wide enough to see the whole, and thus put a stop to any evolution of the mind.

A tree is an extension of the earth. A tree is part of the sun, because the rays of the sun are its life. A tree does not end at its roots. It is an organ of Gaia. The tree is Gaia and Gaia is the tree. It is living earth. A man is not a man, he is an extension of the earth. A man and a woman are part of the sun because the rays of the sun are their life. A tree, a man and a woman are the same because they are an extension of the earth. When they are alive, they are together because they are the same. When they die they go on together, because they are still the same.

The scientists who still presume to offer the public a materialistic view of nature as if it were a received truth, are themselves very largely under the sway of the institution. And so, ultimately, is the cybernarchy. States set aside money for science. Institutions receive a share of that money and the share is given out to individuals for their research. Since science is expensive, control over the individual scientist is therefore complete. The ruling technocrats of the time design exactly what science they want to have. Fashion has always ruled science just as resolutely as it controls art.

During my fifteen years as a university scientist, I made many friends who were deeply driven towards the aims of the natural philosophers, people who loved nature and sought to understand a little about it: men and women of poetic and imaginative enthusiasm who exulted in the priceless beauties of the life-form. But sadly, over the years I watched many of them, first of all starved of research money, and then subjected to all the vindictive and bullying pressures for which the academic bureaucratic community is so notorious, until they gave in and directed their talents towards the prestige goals set by the state scientific committees holding the purse strings. The committees were always managed by older men with honours and titles, who 'rage against the dying of the light' and turn, at bay, finally to visit their frustration upon the young.

The state makes servant toymakers of young natural philosophers, and, by so doing, systematically wrecks their vision. But fortunately, inside the dehumanizing bars and grids of the emergent cybernarchy, there are just as many people who, although they do presently help to make the system work, would also like to see it *cease* to work. There are many bureaucrats and dignitaries of science and the administration who to my certain knowledge desperately want to be freed of the awesome trappings of the state reward system, and who secretly despise the empty surrogates of knighthood, FRS or Nobel Prize: institutional awards which are as ashes in the mouth of the natural philosopher.

The reward and punishment conditioning systems of the institutions are heavily entrenched, and show little sign yet of change. The toymakers firmly control the nature of present technology, and they too will certainly not change their grip voluntarily. But if enough people firmly and permanently reject as many of the *products* of the high technological society as possible and simultaneously reject the purely materialistic analysis of the old science, then eventually the system will be forced to change. Finally, if some of the people who are at present managing the system begin to understand the *force majeure* of survival within the earth organism, the cybernetic state entity is not yet nearly at an advanced enough level of evolution to function without them, and so it will collapse.

The cybernarchy is still vulnerable. The most effective form of attack would be to convince its human operators that they are aiding and abetting the evolution of a new species which is likely to dispense with its human collaborators as and when it has achieved sufficient knowledge and operational capability. I have met a large number of computer engineers and systems specialists, either singly or in my seminars, who freely admit the possibility that the old science fiction cliché of 'the machines taking over' is a genuine possibility, but prefer not to do anything about it since to do so would put their employment at risk.

It is the bureaucrats and the toymakers who need to be convinced that a post-industrial age of Gaia lies before us as a gift. But yet another obstacle still stands in the way, and that is state-controlled education.

At present, state school curricula are aimed at producing adults who will work the industrial system: people who will be able to press the keys of an electric typewriter or computer keyboard according to their logical and manual ability. It seems as though the official curricula are deliberately designed to produce adults with limited skills, who fit the system but are otherwise almost completely deskilled. A child who thinks that vegetables grow in cardboard boxes is deskilled to a tragic degree. If he really does not know where vegetables come from, and if he lives in a tower block in the centre of a city, he will be quite likely to starve to death in the conditions of a general strike.

In my view, in spite of hundreds of devoted teachers who would rather teach the gentle freedoms, current state educational curricula in the West are little more than a conditioning process wherein children are trained as units for the emergent cybernarchy.

I suggest the following basis for a new curriculum, suitable for children of a Gaian age:

1. *Food*: The basics of farming and diet. The cases for industrialized and non-industrialized farming compared.
2. *Warmth*: The heating of a person and the heating of a home. The fossil fuel and the natural energy case compared.
3. *Clothing*: Styles and fashions analysed on the basis of the origin of the materials of the clothing.

4. *Shelter*: Houses through the ages. High- and low-energy buildings. Insulation and materials.
5. *Health*: The self-management of the body in health and illness. Health in relation to lifestyle.
6. *The Planet*: A general studies course which links the foregoing subjects in terms of practical living.

Although this is a mere sketch, it would give as much opportunity for children to acquire reading, writing and arithmetic as the conventional curriculum, but would place these subjects in a secondary position to learning about prime needs.

The emerging cybernarchy must be dismantled, not only because it prevents people choosing a low entropy lifestyle, and not only because it is an evolving industrial entity, but because it stands directly in the way of an expanded vision.

To be able to see the spectre of the tree above its seed; to be able to feel the flow of life and to recapture ancient vision; to be able to recognize in the most central part of our beings that our flesh and blood is the *same* as the green sap of a leaf and the fur of an animal; to recognize the interlocked rhythms of all the species around us and to know that death is a trivial event where our temporary mobile existence submerges like the sphere flattening out on to the infinite plane of life; to know that the rational, logical, reductionist analysis of nature is magnificently, splendidly and absolutely wrong; and to know that the cybernarch is both alien, hostile and irrevocably *other*: these are the necessities for Gaian vision.

28

A Gaian Science

There is perennial debate about the 'human condition', about our essential nature, about whether we are good or bad, loving or hating, civilized or feral. Are we capable of altruism, or simply aggressive predators? How do we relate to each other and what sort of groups should we live in?

This is no more than a statement of my own belief, since it has been the bedrock of my experience so far, but I am convinced that underlying whatever we may understand as 'human nature', there is in everyone a very deep-seated sensitivity towards the needs of the natural world. This ancient and beautifully natural quality probably took origin somewhere in the dim webs of the universal unconscious, and the roots of its formation extend back through the centuries to a time, perhaps, when there were no written languages or machines, when humans were linked to the earth organism by necessity. Everyone still has the elements of this quality down in the recesses of the mind. However wild or civilized, however rich, poor or aggressive a person may be, this quality is, I believe, part of a universal knowledge and understanding which has been remorselessly suppressed by the industrial age. It is an actual part of the mind of Gaia, a genuine connection between our own self-awareness and the earth organism.

The quality of this knowledge, is, by itself, neither good nor bad, beautiful nor ugly. It is neither kind nor cruel, generous nor mean. But it can become a conscious manifestation in our own minds of the 'intelligence' of Gaia, if we reject the unsustainable promises of the machine society.

What is so attractive about this extended vision? Why search for it through change? Why not just go on assuming that the church of reason is undisturbed, that its priests still offer received truths that technology will always provide? First because, as I have tried to show, high technology will not and cannot provide a sustainable future; second because the entropy crisis resulting from high technology will destroy us unless we stop creating disorder; and third because the search for a missing faculty *provides an optimistic and consuming purpose for living*. It forges a link between changes in the way we live and our relationship with Gaia. And it can form an unbreakable defence against the conditioning pressures of the toymakers.

It is a matter of picking up where we left off as integrated members of the Gaian life-form, at the beginning of the machine society: at five seconds to midnight. And it is about expanding consciousness beyond the boundary of the high technology society to rediscover the natural currents and laws that were there all the time.

But 'expanded consciousness' is a much overworked term and I want to explain exactly what I mean by it.

The toymakers still tell us, albeit with a slightly tremulous voice, that if only enough parts are studied in enough detail, the whole will finally emerge. But it does not. The law of diminishing returns operates in their philosophy. Massive and complex apparatus is still thrown together by almost defeated reduction-ists, to extract the last atomic detail from the life process, and still no truth of any serious value emerges. All the molecular, atomic and biochemical framework of life is now depicted and codified, and yet no remotely unified view is even in sight. It is like breaking a watch with a hammer to see what is inside, and then writing a paper showing that a watch is made of bent gear wheels and broken glass.

I do not now expect the science of the toymakers to produce any more great discoveries. Specialization is in full swing and almost every last alley of minutiae has now been explored. There is practically no communication between the specialities, and so each is forced to accept the findings of the others since each logical method is quite incomprehensible to anyone outside its own area of expertise.

But beyond this failing world of the toymakers an exciting extension of science has occurred, one that has all the potential to evolve towards making an end to separatism and a beginning to a new science: a Gaian science perhaps, which could serve as a basis for an expansion of consciousness directed towards a reawakening of the connection between human self-awareness and the mind of the earth organism.

I have been using the idea of 'separatism' to describe a way of looking at things derived from the science of the toymakers, which assumes that human observers stand apart from the rest of nature and the universe. This way assumes that, because we have language, senses and reasoning power, we can use these qualities to build an intellectual raft, a reliable vantage point from which to make what is still called an 'objective description'. The old science of the toymakers still asserts that the ideal of objectivity will, in the end, lead to an absolute view of reality; that we shall finally assemble a fully codified description of the world about us. And there is a great deal to support such a belief. Within the body of knowledge of the old science there is an extensive and highly consistent library of measurement which lies behind all of our present artefacts. But arising out of one field, an aesthetically pleasing and more poetic view of matter and reality is beginning to emerge. One which shows a new way of looking at our surroundings and which could lead directly towards ideas of unity and the wholeness of nature and away from the ruling paradigms of human-centred objectivity and separatism.

One of the great quests in the old science was to discover the 'ultimate structure of reality and matter', and to show how ideas in this area are changing. I now want to go on a journey down through the scale of size to show how it is that, at a certain point, ordinary ideas about reality not only change entirely, but finally come completely unstuck.

I rap my knuckle against a wooden table and I am reassured by the noise of the rap and the feeling in my knuckle. Both sensations tell me without question that the wood is hard and the table is really there. I can also verify the hard outline of the table with my eyes, and this fits the 'knuckle experience' exactly. I do the same thing with the same table the next day and the next day and everything remains consistent. The table is a real table and I will not have anybody monkeying with the idea that the table is anything except an ordinary table which I can rap.

I now decide that the table is interesting and want to know what it is made of. I appoint myself temporary 'professor of table investigation'. Experience tells me that wood comes from trees and books will tell me what the microscopic structure of wood looks like. Just to verify this, I cut a small shaving from the table, cut very thin slices from the shaving, stain them, mount them on a glass slide and look at them down a light microscope. I am totally reassured. Before me are the beautiful arcades and tunnels of the wood cells. Everything fits the text book.

Then I cut even thinner slices of wood and put them in an electron microscope, which lets me examine the wood at a magnification of two million times. Again I am reassured. A whole landscape of new structural detail emerges and I can even see the dim smudged outlines of individual large molecules in one cell wall. Once again my confidence remains unshaken, because I can compare all these results with those of other 'professors of table investigation'. And at the next 'international conference of table investigators' we can all relax over a drink in the evening and congratulate ourselves expensively on the consistency of our results, and on how well we really do understand what a table is and how nobody else should argue with us.

Back in the laboratory, however, I am subject to some niggling doubts and look vainly around for an even more powerful microscope. But there is no such thing, so I have to go to a chemist and ask him what wood is made of. He tells me that it is mainly cellulose, and that the molecular smudges I have been looking at are real images of groups of real cellulose molecules, and that these molecules are made up of carbon and hydrogen atoms. Still reassured about my belief in the church of reason, I then decide that since the table is made of carbon and hydrogen I had better look into the structure of carbon and hydrogen atoms. And so I begin to study atomic theory.

Now the trouble really begins, and my vision of a Nobel Prize for 'contributions to the science of table investigation' disappears. I cannot rap carbon and hydrogen atoms with my knuckles and I cannot see carbon and hydrogen atoms.

There is much worse in store. I now find that the carbon and hydrogen atoms are made of what I am told are 'elementary particles', and that these have names which distinguish each one from another and cannot under any circumstances be seen.

Each atom has a nucleus and the nucleus is made up of particles called nucleons. There are two varieties of nucleon: the proton and the neutron. Then I find that there are other particles called electrons which are circling the nucleus at very high speeds. I also find that these particles have qualities of mass, spin, electric charge and resonance. Not only can I not rap nucleons or electrons, I cannot see them, touch them or feel them; and I cannot weigh them or spin them or get a shock from them. And I am also asked to accept that the atom in which these very high-speed movements are taking place is nearly all empty space.

I look again at the table. Not only is no part of it in visible motion, it does not give me an electric shock, it is not spinning and it does not resonate. No edge or surface is frothing or seething in motion and no part of it, except for the worm-holes, is empty space.

I go back to the particle physicists, tell them they are liars and demand to be shown an electron or nucleon. I receive the answer that electrons and nucleons cannot be put into bottles and they only have a *tendency to exist*. Physicists here talk about a probability cloud, a phrase which describes the strange situation where, although the particles do have properties which enable differences between them to be measured, no one can say whether such a particle is at a particular location in space at a particular time.

In one leap I have left the world of the hard and tangible and entered a new world where there are no hard edges, but only moving miasmas of change and chance. Nothing is certain any more and nothing can be seen or manipulated by the unaided human eye or hand. The table has disappeared in a cloud of uncertainty. But I can still rap the table – or go quietly mad.

Across the whole history of the old science, one can find references to the latest discovery as being the 'final picture of reality', or to a new particle as being the 'ultimate building block of matter'. But now the search is on for the building block of the building blocks at another order of scale altogether. So far this 'idea of a particle' has not been found experimentally, though it has been given a name invented by James Joyce:[1] 'the Quark'.

So physics is proposing that there is a structure to matter which, from our point of view as naked humans, cannot be perceived. We are asked to accept that the table is composed of wood which is made of cellulose, which is made of carbon and hydrogen atoms, which are made of electrons and nucleons which are made of quarks, which are presumably made of God.

Perhaps Plato was right, that somewhere there is a single archetypal table from which all other tables evolved.

So it is true to say that physicists are beginning to construct a view of matter and reality which no unaided human can possibly verify, and which he is forced to *believe* in, unless he has his own cyclotron and can do his own atomic experiments. He may therefore decide that the whole edifice is bunk, since it requires an act of faith to accept something which his mind tells him is totally unreasonable.

But to help resolve this dilemma, the relationship between the experimenter and his experiment has also come under scrutiny. It used to be thought that an experiment was a closed inviolate system inside its own boundary, and that a scientist just looked in through the boundary.

I have already explained the idea of a system boundary. In a particle physics laboratory, if a physicist wants to measure some properties of an electron, first of all he has to build a device which makes electrons, then he has to build apparatus to observe the electrons before he can carry out his experiment. The electron generator is one system, the electron observing apparatus is another, the physicist is a third, and all have boundaries. Once the experiment is set in motion, the only connection between the generating system and the observing system is the stream of electrons themselves. The physicist is connected to and dependent upon both.

The electron stream is not something existing by itself in space, it is a bridge stretching across space from the generating system to the observing system. All three are an indivisible part of a whole. Alter one and the other two are forced to change.

---

[1] James Joyce. *Finnegans Wake*: 'Three quarks for Muster Mark'.

The implications of this interrelationship are profound. For if either the generating or the observing system is altered, or indeed the electrons themselves, the alteration must affect the other system and so the *electrons can have no independent absolute existence*. The problem has been very clearly stated:

'The observed system is required to be isolated in order to be defined, yet interacting in order to be observed.'[2]

Another way of looking at this fundamental change in ideas of reality has been put forward by a physicist, Geoffrey Chew,[3] who has given it a nice friendly name: 'The bootstrap hypothesis'. He believes that there is no aristocracy of elementary particles, no causative hierarchy in which, to misquote George Orwell, some particles are more equal than others. He calls it a particle democracy:

The bootstrap concept is equivalent to the notion already developed of a democracy ... Each interacting particle is conjectured to be a bound state of those channels with which it communicates, owing its existence entirely to forces associated with the exchange particles that communicate with 'crossed' channels. Each of these latter particles in turn owes *its* existence to a set of forces to which the original particle makes a contribution. *In other words, each particle helps to generate other particles which in turn generate it.*

From this it follows that in the fabric of nature there may be no independent existence of a part. Right down at the limits of scale where we can see some of our own building blocks and also those of Gaia, there is absolute interdependence. This view of things seems to me to make any notion of separateness quite impossible, and to undermine absolutely all concepts of dominance and control of the earth organism.

In a very attractive and lucid book,[4] another physicist, Fritjof Capra, has raised these ideas to the level of an art form. Starting from the position that there is no ultimate causality, he develops the idea of particle interaction, or the democracy of particles, and shows that not only is the fabric of nature indivisible but

[2] Henry Stapp. *Physical Review*. Vol. D.3. 1971 (March).
[3] 'Elementary Particles' by Geoffrey Chew in *The Scientific Endeavour*, Rockefeller Institute Press.
[4] *The Tao of Physics*. Fritjof Capra. Fontana, London 1976.

there is probably no reality other than interaction and change. He then shows that although modern physics is only just beginning to emerge with this idea, it was known to Eastern mystics thousands of years ago. It is not just that the authors of the *Tao-Te Ching* and the *I Ching* were writing statements *similar* to those of contemporary physicists: they are often identical. Capra gives a very large number of examples. He first quotes Robert Oppenheimer:

If we ask, for instance, whether the position of the electron remains the same, we must say 'no'; if we ask whether the electron's position changes with time, we must say 'no'; if we ask whether the electron is at rest, we must say 'no'; if we ask whether it is in motion, we must say 'no'.

Capra then matches this with text from the *Upanishads*:

It moves. It moves not.
It is far and it is near.
It is within all this,
And it is outside of all this.

In translation, the word 'It' here refers to 'reality' or the 'way to understanding'.

If Capra's thesis is right, what seems to have emerged is that the view of matter and reality now emerging from theoretical physics is the same as that held by people who were writing three thousand years ago – people with no high technology, no computers and no accelerators. Unless the people of that time were given knowledge by *culture bearers* from a prior civilization – and this is not to be dismissed as a possibility – we have to admit that the authors of the *Upanishads*, the *Tao-Te Ching* and other classics of Eastern mysticism achieved a vision of reality in centuries B.C. which is only just beginning to emerge from the most advanced machines of the twentieth century A.D. And surely the only conclusion to be drawn is that their minds and language worked in an entirely different way from ours. This difference must surely have been the special sensitivity, the Faculty X of Colin Wilson, which I believe has been attenuated by our adoption of the machine society.

If the people of the ancient East were able to construct a view of things which began from the premise that they, as people, were an inseparable part of a whole and that there was no possibility of understanding without primary acceptance of this view, then we can surely do the same if we alter our way of life sufficiently to allow this belief to emerge again.

We can now cross out the word 'observer' scientist and put in its place 'participant'. And this again is a highly optimistic conclusion: because, like the ancient writers of the Tao, it is possible to acquire a real and substantial understanding of the natural world about us by allowing the whole of our conscious individuality to participate in the natural process, almost as if we were like children. A medieval doctor called Petrus Severinus put it eloquently:

> Go, my sons, sell your fields, your apparel and your rings. Burn your books, buy yourselves strong shoes, wander forth into the mountains, explore the valleys and the deserts, the beaches of the sea and the deepest abysses of the earth. Observe the characteristics of animals, the difference between plants, the minerals and study the origin of everything in existence.
> Learn from the peasants the lore of heaven and earth and do not be ashamed. In such wise and no other will you come to the knowledge of things and their nature.

To learn from the peasants and not the specialists, we need light and vision. Light is all things to all people. To the poet it is ecstasy, to the astronomer it is time and to the artist it is shadows and pigment. But to the physicist, it is rays, quanta and mathematical symbols.

Yet light is a universal connective. Without it there is nothing. We see by light, we live by light and it joins all our separate experiences and existences. It is the one stuff, phenomenon, material, energy, call it what you will, which can make inner and outer experience into one single whole with the living earth organism. So I have used it to try and illustrate what I mean by an expansion of consciousness beyond materialistic analysis.

29

Light Is

The first men saw Gods and wove stories around them. Their world was a place of magic, strangeness and danger, and to survive they had to learn the language of their surroundings. There was no other choice.

The interaction between light and their eyes told them exactly how the life-form of the planet worked. They could sense the patterns of energy pulsing through the crust of the planet. Without knowing of chlorophyll or photosynthesis, quanta or waves, they knew and understood the indissoluble connection between sunlight, green leaves and life. They were wholly part of nature: not for romantic or aesthetic reasons, but because their survival depended on this exact sensitivity.

But from the first geometric description of a light ray by Euclid in 300 B.C. it was almost a certainty that the age of reason and its main result, the industrial age, would occur. Men challenged and destroyed the Gods with mathematics and instruments, and put magic to flight with tales of logic and reason. Light dimmed in the fumes of the machine and technical man stamped the earth with steel boots.

The compulsive toolmakers began to disassemble the fabric of nature; to dissect and forage in search of dominance and control.

Light ceased to be the warm luminance of the sun and became straight rays on a piece of paper: rays to burn the earth.

Light was no longer to do with life, it had become power and death.

After 3,000 years of argument about the nature of light, it can still apparently be corpuscular on Friday, a wave motion on Saturday morning and both simultaneously by Sunday. The science of the toymakers may be in the process of refuting itself and a new integrated and participatory approach to nature emerging. In an age of Gaia, intuition and magic may again become as natural to us as they were to the first men. We may be able to look at light as a single unifying quality, a part of a whole.

Not long ago, a scientist re-created the swirling primeval atmosphere of the earth in his laboratory. He made a warm primitive soup of simple chemicals and struck it with artificial lightning. And out of the chemical womb in his flask, the light and the lightning began to fashion the substances essential to the beginning of life. Millions of years ago, long before scientists and man, the earth was similarly fired with lightning and lit with fierce ultra-violet radiation. The energy of the light created the first life.

Through myth, ritual and religion, ancient peoples understood this ancient power of light, but they had no instruments and no machines to analyse it. Their knowledge was whole and it came from their perceptions, their ideas and their consciousness. They had no analytical methods and no concepts or abstractions like rays, photons or quanta. Their view of light was intuitive. It was to do with magic and religion. And it was to do with growing food and keeping warm. They must have intuitively understood the solar drive chain. They must have had an inner language about the elegant sequence of events starting with the energy of the sun's rays and ending with the growth of plants. If they had not understood, they would not have survived.

The intuition of the sun religions is just as true now as it was then. Without light, there is no life. Light is life and in the darkness there is no life.

One of the oldest ideas in history is that the eye puts out a beam of light. We are used now to the ray diagrams of science showing how light behaves. But rays and geometry do not show what light is. They show abstractions, directions and ideas of movement.

There have been four great ideas about light, and each shows an alternative view of nature. The first came from the platonists of Greece, who believed that no rays came from the object to the eye, but instead there was a mysterious 'empathy' or spirit connecting the two. They held that awareness was only the power of the will: not rays, just a relationship of body, spirit and nature.

The second view held that rays from the eye light up the object, and this was the first idea of action at a distance, something going from the eye to the object.

Following the idea of action at a distance, Euclid drew the first ray diagrams of light and so started the inevitable shift towards analytical optics and its stark view of reality. Later on, Roger Bacon came to believe that once the rays had left the eye they took on a life of their own and scanned the object like vibrating rods.

The third view was that rays from the eye and rays from the object met and interacted in space. And the fourth view, the one we have today, is that the object sends out rays to the eye.

Each set of ideas is absolutely different, and yet their sequence shows a direct pathway to the age of reason. From the first rays of Euclid, through action at a distance and on to radiating objects, it was almost inevitable that finally Newton would put a prism in the way of a beam of sunlight in the way that I have already described.

Newton believed that all the colours were revealed by his prism, and that they were already present in the white light of the sun. But Goethe held instead that Newton's colours were manufactured by the light, and that it was the conflict between a dark object and the light which created colours:

When there is no light, there is only darkness. But darkness is not the absence of light. It is a real substance. I can see darkness just as I can see light. They are to me more like the opposite poles of a magnet: each necessary to each other.

The differences between the two men are symbolic of a great division. The *onlooker* scientists like Newton believed that nature could be understood from an isolated position. The *participants* like Goethe believed that knowledge could only be achieved by studying nature from within.

Goethe linked life, nature and light together in one indivisible whole. He refused to accept the light-ray as truth but saw light as life.

The energy in the light of the sun maintains all life. It powers vegetables, diatoms, monkeys and men alike. We all turn towards the light, like flowers to the sun. We are all unified by light. The light of the sun holds the earth together. Light created the eye and the eye created the light. They are part of the same whole. Vision is the creation of a model of the outside world inside our head.

It is not the reductionist views of light and vision that are wrong. They reveal a marvellous machine, and beautiful relationships. But they show nothing beyond. They are a useful preliminary to an understanding of an extended consciousness. Science as a value-free system has shut itself away inside limits set by itself, and fails to show our absolute unity with the earth organism, because it has destroyed its own antennae. To state that nature is value-free is just as strong a statement of belief as to say there is a God.

After Newton, there came the great divide between 'corpuscles' and 'undulants'. To one observer, light was a wave; to another it was quanta: individual packets of energy. But truly spoken, light is photons and quanta and other qualities. It is fire, as a lens concentrates the sun to burn a piece of paper. It is mass and energy, when a laser burns a hole in a sheet of metal. It is movement, when the radiometer vanes rotate in the glass globe under a hail of light. Without light there is darkness and in darkness there is no need of an eye. If the universe were dark there would have been no eyes. Light connects the eye to the universe. Light is information: it is a path of evolution and it is a direct path of extended consciousness.

As we move out along the bridge of what the ancients would have called the 'eye-ray', we can look up and down time. History is not the past, it is a bridge of light travelling down through time. The history of the universe still moves towards us borne on ever expanding spheres of light.

If entities looked at us from the Andromeda galaxy, they would see only the first men, since earth light takes centuries to reach them. We can never see the Andromedans, only their ancestors. Even if we look at our own face in the mirror, we do not see ourselves – because of the finite speed of light, we only see ourselves as we were an instant in the past.

Light can destroy like a laser beam burning a village, but only in the hands of the toymakers. These are forms of light hammered and forged by the toymakers. They are unnatural light: light tamed, distorted, amplified and deformed. In perfecting the geometry and mathematics of light, its essence has escaped altogether. By predatory over-use of knowledge, the toymakers have lost wisdom.

But participatory science lets us see our relationship to the whole. It is a view of things that brings back all the magic and wisdom of the ancients and mixes them with the sophistications of technical science.

The modern, participant scientific view of light is that the apparent paradox of waves and particles vanishes in the theory of complementarity: a view which does not invalidate science but extends it in a strikingly imaginative direction. Now it is accepted quite easily that the wave and quantum are different models of the same thing: both are frameworks to which some of the properties of light can be fitted.

But the idea of the complementarity of opposites is almost as old as written language, as Fritjof Capra has pointed out. The authors of the Tao achieved this wisdom inside their minds with intuitive consciousness alone, without the accelerators and synchrotrons of modern physics.

It was partly despair that led physicists like Bohr and Heisenberg to lay the foundations of complementarity. Indeed it was Heisenberg, in a famous speech to the University of Saxony, who said:

Almost every scientific advance is bought at the cost of renunciation, almost every gain in knowledge sacrifices important standpoints and established modes of thought. As facts and knowledge accumulate, the claim of the scientists to an *understanding* of the world in a certain sense *diminishes*.

All knowledge whether it be old or new tells us that we are all part of the same 'stuff', the same substance and the same being as the light. As we change, so does the light change. And as the light changes, so do we change as well. Analysis alone can lead only to intellectual exhaustion and despair.

Many groups of people, some of whom were initially trained

in the techniques of reductionist analysis, now live their lives in a way which is directly linked to the idea of a whole in which light becomes a single great creative generality.

The people of Findhorn I have already referred to have created an extraordinary bond between man, light and plant. They have turned relatively infertile soil in a bleak area of Scotland into a rich profusion of plant growth. Not by techniques alone, but by *participation* with light and plant.

One of the oldest ideas is that living things have an aura, a surrounding halo of light which only some can see. No scientist had ever recorded an aura, but in 1939 in Krasnodar in Russia, Semion and Valentina Kirlian began work in this strange field. Semion had always been intrigued by the sparking which occurs in high-frequency electrical apparatus. And so he wondered whether the sparks would expose a photographic plate, a totally illogical thought which produced extraordinary results. After burning himself severely, he finally began to get pictures of living things surrounded by a strange glowing halo, much like the aura of the ancients.

These outlandish results were immediately attacked by physicists, who complained that they were nothing more than a 'corona discharge', a description which is certainly part of the truth. Opinion became violently divided. Believers said: 'The Kirlian Light is the light of the spirit.' Sceptics said: 'I see nothing remarkable, photographic emulsion is exposed by many effects.'

No one is certain what these strange images are due to, but the changes in halo, for example, in a leaf as it dies are extraordinary. When the leaf is first taken from its plant, the Kirlian effect around it is bright and sharp, but gradually the light disappears as the leaf 'dies'.

If the hands of a healer are photographed, the Kirlian aura around them is bright, pointillistic and sharp. After healing, the aura is reduced and muted, as if the energy of the healer had in some way been temporarily drained and transferred to the body of the patient.

The analytical, reductionist approach to these unusual effects is to take them apart, and send each part to the specialist. The electrical engineer will have one view, the photochemist who knows about the effect of light on photographic emulsions will have another, and a physiologist may comment on sweat changing the resistance of the skin. All three specialists may lose sight of the possibility that the Kirlian light is a manifestation of real changes related to a more unified effect which connects light, people and healing.

As in the light hologram where the whole of a picture is expressed in any single part of a film negative, the new science is extending towards new visions of a unified nature, where we are total participants and where the whole is in the part.

Analysis and reductionism have, in the end, produced only a highly detailed chaos. As each research project closes, so does it generate a new set of unknowns in its wake. As the last molecule is prised loose, so does the whole vanish in a flurry of waves and equations until there is nothing but the despair of the isolated intellect.

There is no real *difference* between the parts of nature we can perceive. In a unified view of things we can move easily from the flaming corona of the sun to tiny circular algae which have the same shape and also flare with light. We can go from the spiral of a seashell to the spiral of a distant galaxy and *exult* in the congruence of the shapes. We can peer down microscopes at the swirling of the cytoplasm in living cells, and then up into the rotating star systems of deep space. We can match the spouting brilliance of volcanoes to the jutting plasmas of a solar prominence. And we can *feel* the link between the tiny luminescence of insects and the speckles of moonlight on water.

Gaia is all of life and all of the rocks. Within the universal intelligence of the one single living earth organism is the way to a genuine expansion of wisdom and an ultimate experience of beauty. Just as Gaia is conscious, so too are we conscious. If we truly want to know ourselves, then we must first know Gaia.

30

Epilogue

One evening I was alone in my university laboratory looking down at the screen of an electron microscope. It was quiet, the room was dark and on the screen was a greenish electronic image of a small slice of animal skin. One part of one cell was in view at a magnification just high enough to show some of the larger molecules of the wall of the skin cell. In effect I was looking at the molecules of the surface of the animal: where the animal stopped and where the rest of the universe began.

One of the odd discoveries which comes from looking at cells at these very high magnifications is that all species look very much alike. It is often impossible to distinguish animal from human from plant cell material.

Slowly, while I was looking in through the hard vacuum of the microscope column, I began to understand that in life there were atoms in the air, oxygen and nitrogen stretching beyond the skin of the animal like an interwoven lacework of matter connecting the skins of all animals, all plants and all humans. And then I saw very clearly that all living and non-living materials can only interact in the way I described in the last section. I also saw images which told me that they are all interconnected and so, in this microscope sense, are all one single whole.

Much later I saw the pictures again in a waking dream. The universe had become a swirling mass of atoms: a limitless blizzard of small dark specks flurrying and colliding in a dynamic dance of interaction. Then people, animals and plants started to appear through the storm of specks as moving silhouettes, pencilled in only slightly more heavily than the outlines of the atoms. They were not surfaced like the skin of an animal or the surface of a leaf, but appeared more like a picture drawn with a very soft pencil on rough paper. It was as if the outlines of the living beings were not only able to move easily through the storm of specks but that the specks were also moving through the surfaces of the life-forms in a perpetual interaction. As the living things moved through the blizzard of atoms, they appeared constantly to dissolve and re-form as the clouds of whirling matter flowed effortlessly through them. The life-forms were not hard and unyielding, pushing the atoms aside, but soft outlines moving like wraiths right through the network of the universe. They were constantly changing events, not structures. There was a complete whole of motion, change and interaction and I had the very strong sense that I was experiencing a total integration of events and structures in which I too was a dynamic interacting part. I realized that the static image in the microscope was only a frozen event.

From this time on, it has been impossible for me to maintain the idea that my skin limits my individuality. My body only allows my thoughts to move about, my hands to make things, and my senses and experience to travel the planet I live on. But as I move, the matter of the universe moves through me as easily as the wind through the branches of trees.

For a while, this discovery left me thoroughly ill at ease. I was unable to cope with the implication. I simply had no language. It was not until some months afterwards that I realized the experience was the beginning of a personal liberation from the confining dogmas of reductionist science. Not only was everything connected to everything else, but everything *was* everything else, and to see this very simple truth did not mean a rejection of reason, but, as Laurens van der Post has put it, a rejection of the *tyranny* of reason.

Just as in the 'bootstrap hypothesis' each elementary particle only exists because of its interaction with the forces of another, so do I exist only by the interaction of my physical body with the molecules of the sky, the ground and the water.

From then on any pretence of separation was unthinkable. It was completely unreasonable to suppose that I could ever be an island entity sweeping aside the particles of the universe and then gathering them together again inside an instrument for study. This experience occurred some years ago and was the first of a series which has led me to write this book and change the direction of my life entirely.

It has taken me all of my life so far to realize that the single great obstacle in the way of survival and an extended human vision is the industrial society itself, and its expropriation and suppression of the most sensitive and creative qualities of the mind. But as I move slowly along the path of changes, I have had several other experiences which have convinced me, just on a personal level, that I am on the right track. Several have been so intense as to alter my awareness completely, and they have all been to do with a cessation of thinking and a beginning of being.

On one occasion, I was looking at a ripening field of barley and was concluding on a rather intellectual level, 'what a beautiful colour' – without any real involvement in the thought. Then I went on to think over the views I have tried to express here, and then, without warning, my mind shut off and everything went quiet and I began to be aware in an entirely different way. The gradations of colour and the waves of the wind undulating through the hairs of the grain became a nearly unbearably intense experience: a feeling of beauty which I have never before known. Every sense intensified to a level where I cried out in delight. The colours became a whole event complete and unanalysable: they were touchable, I could smell them and feel them, they were all shades of gold and brown. Their intensity almost burnt into my eyes. I was the grain, I was the colours. I have no way of knowing, in clock time, how long this experience lasted, but it ceased just as suddenly as it began and gradually my ordinary brain began to think again.

On another occasion I was thinking about the idea of the solar drive chain, and how our whole survival is linked to the radiance of the sun passing into the green leaves by the miraculous process of photosynthesis. Then again without warning, a similar change occurred. I moved without effort or choice into a different mode of perception. Again I stopped thinking and started to be the leaves, to be the green sap and to be the radiance of the sun. I became totally immersed in a warm green living sea of luminance where I no longer had to breathe, and although I was under the surface of the fluid, there was no possibility of drowning, since breathing was unnecessary. Life and sustenance were flowing into my skin directly. I did not move, my breathing appeared to stop, and I did not think. The whole of the living green flowed through me like the outlines passing through atoms of the universe. The experience is difficult to describe and I have found it impossible to illustrate the force of its influence on me. During the time it lasted – and again I do not know how long – there was no room for thought and the whole of my consciousness was taken up and propelled into a whole, where I became completely still.

Part of my head still makes disagreeably rational noises about 'overtiredness', 'delusion' and 'eidetic imagery', but not much of it. The words are useless tautologies. The experience was a strikingly different experience of an extended reality, and it showed me that by changing mental set, there is an infinite potential for evolution and change. During these times, my consciousness, my being, is open to the thread of connection I wrote about earlier, which stretches between the envelope of my individual existence and the living universal mind of Gaia: the neck connecting the sphere to the plane of the continuum.

I spent years of my life studying the flesh and blood of the human body, and learned the functions of the beautifully integrated systems of support, action, pumping and communication. I saw how each part, each organ and network functioned as a self-repairing and stable complex with its own apparent boundary. I visualized the lungs exchanging gases, the liver creating a complex of chemicals and the eyes writing codes about the outside world for the leaseholder of the body to comprehend.

The body, in reality, is a microcosm of Gaia. Just as animals relate to the plants, and cycles of stability in the biosphere maintain the continuum of life among the species, so do the organs of the body all interrelate to create a stable whole.

But just as the body is mortal, so may Gaia also be. The earth organism may die in its time, just as a bacterium may in seconds, a mayfly in a day and a man after three score years and ten. There is very probably a natural limit to the existence of all living systems, simple or complex, small or large, and eventually the earth may be lifeless for a second time.

The motes of life are probably scattered across the universe, waiting for an unknown pattern of circumstances to draw them all together in one place at one time. Perhaps in the frozen centre of a comet streaking across the depths of space beyond the limits of our stars, those motes, mere fragments of molecules, are already gathering to land on the warm surface of a planet orbiting a distant star. It is not really important if the earth organism eventually dies, but knowing all that we know and possessing all the responsibility that we can possess, we have an absolutely clear choice of whether we hasten that death or help its natural span. And that is important.

The way to an age of Gaia is going to be difficult and hazardous. There are real risks in the changes themselves and there will be resolute and aggressive opposition from the proponents of the toymaking society. So, very considerable persistence will be necessary. Perhaps when the going gets too hard, additional sources of strength will be needed. So to end my book, here is part of a medieval appeal to the goddess of the earth. It is anonymous.

Holy Goddess Earth, parent of nature, who dost generate all things, and regenerate the planet which thou alone showest to the folk upon earth: Thou guardian of heaven and sea, and arbiter of all the gods, by whose influence Nature is wrapt in silence and slumber, thou art she who restorest day and puttest the darkness to flight, who governest the shades of night in all security, restraining at thy will the mighty chaos, winds and rain and storms, or again letting them loose. Thou churnest the deep to foam, and puttest the sun to flight, and arousest the tempests, or again at thy pleasure thou sendest forth the glad daylight: thou givest us food in safety by a perpetual covenant; and, when our soul fleeth away, it is in thy bosom that we find our haven of rest.

For the first time in our history, we have enough knowledge and skill to create an infinitely sustainable future of great personal reward, or a quick and universal death. The choice is ours alone.